Books by Ephraim Kishon

Blow Softly in Jericho

Ephraim Kishon

Blow Softly in Jericho

TRANSLATED FROM THE HEBREW BY YOHANAN GOLDMAN

Atheneum NEW YORK 1970

And the children of Israel who straitly shut up Jericho became tired of the heavy war and compassed the city in a big demonstration and carried placards saying, We want peace! Enough of conquests! Make love, not war! So did they.

And the people shouted with a great shout and blew with the trumpets in protest.

And Joshua adjured them at the time, saying, Stop that racket, ye'll bring down the walls on us.

They did. And they took the city of Jericho also, and the war in the wilderness continues, woe to the victors.

Contents

Contents

Blow Softly in Jericho

❧ *Ever since delivery from Egyptian bondage, the Jewish people have been considered the unflinching champions of freedom. More than that, we were the first to legislate the liberation of slaves, in all sorts of revolutions we carried high the banner of equality between man and man, and now in our new fatherland we have at long last freed from its bonds the Jewish washing machine as well.*

Born to Be Free

One evening not long ago, the wife informed me that we needed a new washing machine, since the old one was overtaxed by our country's climatic conditions. What the little one meant was that in winter we expected an extra effort from the washing machine since it has to launder every single piece of underwear at least three times because of the rain maliciously wetting what is hung outdoors to dry. In view of the particularly rainy season, there was no doubt at all that we needed a younger and more virile machine.

"All right," I gave the little one the green light, "go and buy a washing machine, but just one and as locally manufactured as you can find."

She is very good at buying, the little one. The very next day a Hebrew washing machine with highly polished knobs, a long cord and instructions was humming pleasantly on our paved kitchen patio. It was love at first wash, as the ads say lately. It did all the washing automatically from soaping to wringing, as if endowed with human intelligence.

And that is exactly what the story is about.

At noon on that Tuesday the wife came into my study and said, somewhat upset: "Ephraim! Our machine is walking!"

I followed her at the double to the kitchen patio and there beheld the contraption engaged in "spin drying" and at the same time moving with remarkable hops toward the kitchen. We stopped it literally on the threshold by pressing the red panic button, and sized up the situation. We found that it walked only while spin drying, as then the drum spun at a dizzying speed, the body of the contraption started vibrating terribly and—hop! hop! hop!—it was impelled forward by an uncontrollable inner urge.

We did not attach too much importance to this phenomenon. After all, our home is not a prison and if the machine felt like taking a spin on the patio, why, that's OK with us.

One stormy night we were awakened by the scrunch of tortured metal coming from the patio and, going out there, we found Amir's tricycle completely smashed, lying under our spin-drying machine. The kid howled at the top of his voice and beat his little fists against the sides of the wayward appliance: "Phooey, naughty laundry, phooey!"

"I won't take any chances," the woman decided, "I'll tie Jonathan up!"

She took a piece of rope and tied the appliance to the hot-water tap. I didn't feel too good about this, but did not intervene—after all, it was her machine and thus she had the right to tie it up if she felt like it. But I can't, nor do I want to, deny that next morning I felt most sympathetic when we found Jonathan on the other side of the patio. He had put his horsepowers to work and snapped the rope. The woman gritted her teeth and tied it up again, this time to the gas tanks.

The ear-splitting racket sparked off by this act will forever linger in my memory.

"Ephraim," the woman whispered, "it's dragging the gas tanks along."

The copper pipe was bent to breaking point and there was a penetrating smell of cooking gas in the air. We realized it would not be wise to tie up Jonathan again since he obviously resented it. After this incident we left him to his laundering in complete freedom. Somehow we got used to the idea that our washing machine was a noble Israeli animal which would not tolerate any kind of rein. Only once, on a Saturday night, it caused an unpleasant incident when it burst into the parlor and started annoying our guests.

"Out," the wife screamed, "get out! Back to your kennel!"

As if a washing machine could understand what one is saying to it! Ridiculous, isn't it? I pressed the red button and stopped it dead in its tracks. When the guests had left I restarted Jonathan so as to lead him back, but it seems that he was past the "spin dry" stage and, as will be remembered, this was his only ambulatory stage. We had to go through the whole process again, a lengthy operation.

In the meantime Amir had made great friends with the machine. He rode all day long on Jonathan, shouting: "Giddy-up, giddy-up!"

Very nice. Jonathan also launders extremely well, goes easy on the washing powder. Indeed, except for his penchant toward side trips, we have no complaints against him. However, on one of those murky afternoons he gave me a bad scare. I came home through the garage and there was spinning Jonathan coming toward me in huge jumps. If I had been just a few minutes later he would have reached the road through the open garage door.

"Say," the wife mused, her eyes dreaming. "Couldn't we send him to do the shopping at the supermarket?"

There was nothing we could do but consult a specialist. With a heavy heart I went to see the representative of the factory and told him our tale of woe. The specialist was not a bit surprised.

"Yes, yes," he agreed. "They run when they spin. But only if you put too little laundry in the drum. In that case a centrifugal imbalance is created which pushes the machine forward. Fill Jonathan up with at least four kilos of laundry and he won't budge from his spot, I promise."

I came back from the specialist filled with satisfaction and joy. I found the little one weeding in the garden. I told her that for lack of enough dirty linen our machine was running centrifugally amuck.

The wife blanched. "Good Lord," she stuttered, "today I put just two kilos in it."

We hurried to the patio and the world went black before our eyes. Jonathan had disappeared. Shouting hoarsely, I burst into the road.

"Jonathan! Jonathan!"

I sped along the houses and asked the neighbors whether they had seen a Hebrew-speaking washing machine walking toward the city. The neighbors shook their heads regretfully. One of them asked what color the machine was; another remarked that he seemed to remember seeing something like that in front of the post office, but we found that it was a refrigerator some porters had carelessly left there.

After a long and fruitless search I returned home utterly dejected. Who knows, perhaps in the meantime a bus had run down the poor kid—those drivers were all maniacs. Tears were in my eyes. Our Jonathan, freedom-loving son of our industrial jungle, was now facing all the dangers of the big city's wild traffic. Should his "spin dry" stop in the middle of the road, he would no longer be able to move . . . and would stand there . . . in the middle of Allenby Road. . . .

"He's here!" The woman came running toward me. "He's here!"

What had happened was that while the wife was innocently weeding the garden, the little idiot had stepped into the hallway, skipped toward the basement steps and had been stopped at the very last moment when he inadvertently pulled the plug out from the wall, a deed which saved him from a certain crash.

"Enough!" the wife decided. "Take off your underwear!"

And since then she has been collecting all the potential laundry to be found in our house, stuffing Jonathan with four and a half kilos of washing. And indeed, since then Jonathan has not budged an inch. It's all he can do to breathe and turn the top-heavy drum within his belly.

"Poor fellow," I mumbled seeing him so brutally immobilized, "it's a shame to do this to him."

Yesterday something snapped within me. I quietly stopped him at "spin" and removed at least a kilo and a half. Jonathan again started frolicking gaily and made a beeline for the pretty Italian washing machine across the street, sounding a happy masculine rumble—just like old times.

I patted his trembling flanks. "Go, Jonathan, go!"

He was born to be free.

❧ *Somehow or other, one can cope with a frolicsome washing machine, because its vocabulary is somewhat limited. But the situation becomes critical if one has to face a computer of Jewish origin. To the best of our knowledge, the monster computer of the Ministry of Finance in Jerusalem is the only one in the world that ever notified its superiors: "Gentlemen, yesterday afternoon I went out of my mind, over."*

The Jerusalem Golem

One evening not long ago I received a note from the State of Israel Revenue Department. It was only an official slip of paper written in shaky print, saying: *"Last warning before seizure. Since you have not acted on our notifications regarding your debt to the amount of IL20,012.11 in payment of repairs carried out in the Kishon River Harbor in July 1961, may I draw your attention to the fact that unless you pay the above debt within seven days we shall apply to you the provisions of the law regarding the seizure of your property and its sale."* Thus the words of the Revenue Department, somewhat tempered by the last paragraph: *"If in the meantime you have settled your debt, please disregard this notification."* Signed: *"S. Seligson, Department Head."*

Slight panic seized me upon receiving this letter.

On the one hand, a careful examination of my books proved beyond the shadow of a doubt that no repair work had been carried out on me lately, but on the other hand I could not claim by any stretch of the imagination that I had settled the above matter with the authorities in the words of the warning. And since I am for the settlement of local conflicts by direct negotiation, I went to the Revenue Department and had a personal talk with Mr. Seligson.

"Here," I said, showing him my identity card. "I am a writer and not a river."

The Department Head looked at me closely. "Then why are you called Kishon?"

"It's a habit," I set things right. "But I'm also Ephraim, and the river isn't."

That did it. The Head apologized and went to the next room in order to discuss the painful matter with his associates. They conferred in hushed tones, looked in from time to time, and once asked me to turn around with raised hands. In the end they were convinced of the validity of my case, or at least gave me the benefit of the doubt. The Head of the Department, Seligson, came back and canceled the warning, writing on my file in red pencil: *"He has no harbor! Seligson."* He also drew a big zero on the file and crossed it through with a diagonal line. I returned to my family greatly relieved.

"It was an error," I informed the wife. "Sheer logic won out."

"You see," the woman replied. "One shouldn't lose heart straight away."

The *"Note on the Seizure of Chattels"* arrived on Wednesday noon. *"Since you did not act on the 'Warning Before Seizure of Chattels' and did not pay*

your debt to the amount of IL20,012.11," Mr. Seligson
wrote me in the same shaky print, *"I shall be forced to
apply the provisions of the law regarding the seizure of
chattels in your house and business. If in the meantime
you have settled your debt, consider this note as canceled."*

I went to the Department on the double.

"Yes, yes," Mr. Seligson tried to calm me. "These
notes are sent out by the electronic computer in Jerusalem and not by me. It keeps doing this sort of thing,
don't worry about it."

It seems that the computing center in Jerusalem
introduced automation about a half a year ago, in the
spirit of the twentieth century, and since then the computer has been doing the job of ten thousand sad-eyed
clerks. The computer's only shortcoming is that the
local technicians don't yet know exactly how it works
and occasionally feed it data which give it indigestion,
as in the case of the harbor repairs. Mr. Seligson promised me that this time the delicate matter would be settled once and for all, and just to be on the safe side, he
sent a teleprinter message to Jerusalem: until further
notice the handling of my debt should be deferred, on
his responsibility. I thanked him for the noble gesture,
and returned to my family in excellent spirits.

On Sunday morning they took away the refrigerator. Three brawny Government porters produced an
order signed by S. Seligson and then seized my refrigerator and moved it through the door and into the street.
I hopped and skipped around them like a startled
rooster.

"Am I a river?" I crowed. "Where am I a river?

Can a river talk? Can a river jump around?"

Actually, the men were only doing their job. I found Mr. Seligson at the office in an utterly dejected mood. Early in the morning a note had reached him from Jerusalem, a first warning about his debt to the amount of IL20,012.11 for repairs on me.

"It seems," he told me, his eyes reproachful, "that the computer interpreted the words 'on my responsibility' in this way! One has to be very careful! You put me in a nice fix, my dear sir, I must say!"

I told him that he should regard the note as canceled, but the man was completely hysterical.

"Once the computer gets hold of you, there's nothing you can do about it!" He tore his hair. "Only two months ago the head of the Execution Department received an order from the Jerusalem computer to execute his deputy. Only the Minister's personal intervention saved the fellow at the last minute. His head was literally taken out of the noose."

I proposed that we take a taxi, go up to Jerusalem and have a man-to-man talk with the machine. "Sir," we'd say to it, "kindly recheck your data!"

"You can't talk to it," thus Seligson, "it's the busiest computer in the area—they use it for forecasting the weather and interpreting dreams as well."

Just the same, he rang the storeroom of the Jaffa Department and gave orders to defer the sale of my refrigerator until further notice. The refrigerator was sold the same evening at a public auction for IL19 in cash, as transpired from the *"Statement of Debt"* which reached my house next morning in a most unbureaucratic way. My debt had shrunk to IL19,993.11, which must be settled within seven days. If in the meantime . . .

I waited over an hour for Seligson to come to his office. He had been rushing all over town with his lawyer, had registered his refrigerator in his wife's name, and swore that if ever he got out of the computer's clutches he would never again intervene on anyone's behalf. I asked him what was going to happen to me now.

"I don't know," Seligson answered, breathing heavily. "Sometimes it happens that the computer forgets somebody for months on end, so let's hope . . ."

I told him that I couldn't trust in miracles, I believed in more concrete things; I wanted to settle the affair once and for all. "As you like," Seligson said, "you have every right." After a brief but stormy argument, we reached an agreement according to which I would pay for the repair of my harbor in twelve monthly installments. I signed the undertaking and we sent a notification on this to Jerusalem in order to save what could still be saved on my chattels.

"This is the best I can do," Seligson apologized. "I'm convinced that in two or three years' time the computer team will get more proficient, but meanwhile I'm sorry."

"Never mind," I consoled him. "One can't have everything at once."

The first check in the amount of IL1,666.05 reached me yesterday. Together with the Treasury's check there also arrived Seligson's note, written in the computer's shaky print, to the effect that this was the first payment for the IL19,993.11 with which I was credited in Jerusalem on March 1, 1969. I remarked to the wife that from now on we had no worries in life, whereupon she remarked that it was a shame they didn't pay us interest as well; one gets six percent everywhere.

"Darling," I said to her, "I am sick and tired of the whole matter, I'm not going to move another finger."

The future belongs to automation. Please consider this story as canceled.

❧ *The parking-place explosion is one of mankind's most acute crises, and, except for the Communist Bloc, no one has succeeded in solving the problem. The situation is becoming more critical day by day: in the U.S. there is a car for every fifth person, while in Israel every fifth person is a traffic cop.*

The Espresso Gambit

We were sitting in our favorite café nursing two espressos and throwing longing glances at the NO PARKING sign outside. In the passage, half-frozen flu germs were coughing spasmodically. Dusk was descending at a slanting angle. Ervinke stirred the opaque liquid absent-mindedly: at this time of the day the car-adoption ritual should be just about to start. But the first cop didn't show up till 10:00 P.M.—a lanky trafficker with a rattail mustache and a proud gait. Ervinke waited until the Law drew up in front of a fire-engine-red sports car and pulled out his wad of tickets—then, with perfect timing, dashed out of the café.

"Just a sec," Ervinke gasped, "I only went in for a minute . . . just to have an espresso . . ."

"Sir," thus the Law, "tell that to the judge."

"Now really, officer," Ervinke whined, "be a sport. After all, I'm here now . . ."

"Sir, you are interfering with my work!"

"But I only went in for a minute . . ."

The cop filled out the ticket with sadistic deliberation, then raised a pair of burning eyes. "Look there, sir," he said. "What's written on that sign?"

"Parking forbidden for six meters," Ervinke mumbled contritely. "But just for an espresso, really . . ."

"Sir," thus the cop, "another provocative remark and I'll apply para seventeen as well, for parking too far from the curb."

"See?" Ervinke snorted. "That's why people hate you!"

" 'Para seventeen.' " The cop wrote it down evenly and added: "I'll run you in, sir!"

"But why?"

"I don't owe you explanations, sir. Your papers, please!"

Ervinke handed them over.

"Sir," the Law flared up, "I don't need your Sick Fund card! Where is your driving license?"

"I haven't got one."

"You haven't got one? Very well! 'Para twenty-three'! Have you got a car license, insurance policy?"

"No."

"No?"

"No. Nor have I got a car."

Silence.

Weird, pulsating silence.

"Then," the trafficker whispered, "then to whom does . . . this . . . red sports car . . . belong?"

"How am I to know?" Ervinke shot back. "I only went in for a quick espresso. That's what I've been trying to tell you all along, but you didn't give me a chance."

The cop blanched, turned into anti-matter, his

jaws moving rhythmically. His expression will haunt me for many sleepless nights. Purple-faced, he stuck the ticket on the sports car's windshield and left. At the corner he disintegrated with a sharp report.

Altogether, it had been a pleasant, entertaining evening.

Every citizen departing the country causes us a great deal of heartbreak, but if a football player leaves just because he is offered a measly few thousand dollars, that is a real national disaster. Our sports authorities are doing everything in their power to stop the mass flight, and are offering fabulous sums to everybody involved, except to the players themselves, because that would qualify as appeasement.

The Great Flight

"Is Pommie going to play?"

Yes, that was the question which on that Sabbath afternoon worried the fans of the champion team Lightning-Holon meeting Hapoel Kfar Maccabi in a fateful match of the National League. The excitement was understandable: according to well-informed circles, the team's coach had been given secret orders by the management to keep an eye on the players, and the spectators indeed saw him before the start of the game, running about among the players, counting them and double-checking.

The reason was well known to all: the team scouts had found passports in the effects of several players, among them the legendary Pommie, as the affectionate fans had nicknamed Pomerantz. As a matter of fact, this surprised only those who did not know the real Pommie. This football star extorted from his club everything that could be extorted. Not only had they arranged for him light work—part-time baby-sitter with a childless family—but on top of that they had granted him an increased training bonus as well as overtime. Everybody had thought that Pomerantz was at last satisfied, but about two weeks earlier the player had been seen leaving a bookstore carrying—an English dictionary!

The club had acted promptly: two full-time detectives were hired and assigned to tail Pommie wherever he went. The open clash between Pommie and his club happened on that Wednesday when the player came to the manager and demanded that he, too, be hired as a detective.

"I can tail myself better than anyone else," Pommie explained, "and then at least I'll be able to live on my salary."

"Never!" the manager answered, the veins bulging on his neck. "I won't tolerate professionalism here! We won't sink into the shameful quagmire in which English, Hungarian and Brazilian football has been for many years now. You are a sportsman, Pomerantz!"

"All right, so from now on I want to be considered an entertainer."

"Never," thus the manager. "You shouldn't make your living out of football!"

"Then call it footballet!"

"Never!" The manager raised his voice. "As long as I manage the club at the head of which my party has placed me, I shall not permit ugly professionalism. Because," the manager added, "if they should introduce ugly professionalism, I won't be able to keep my job at the head of the club. Is that clear?"

That sounded logical. Pomerantz left without another word and on that very day ostentatiously bought himself particularly dark sunglasses, as the detectives pointed out in their daily report. The alarming signs quickly increased: suddenly the player's wife appeared to be calm and happy, she dyed her hair blond, then . . . she bought . . . two suitcases!

The entire Football Federation was gripped by panic.

"The situation is serious," the Secretary General frankly admitted to the assembled Executive. "A star player like Pomerantz nets our Federation about a million pounds a year, and yet the bastard is now plotting to flee abroad because they are offering him IL600 a month. What can we do to prevent him from leaving? For goodness sake, what is to be done? What can we do?"

It was indeed a hard question. The Football Federation had already tried everything to instill some order into this important branch of sports. After our loss against Luxembourg (1:14), revolutionary changes were introduced in the Federation's set-up: Hapoel received twelve seats on the Executive—i.e., an additional representative at the expense of Maccabi—and another floor was added to the office building at a cost of half a million pounds. It was then that two fullbacks, a halfback and a slightly used left-wing deserted the National Team and emigrated to Australia, South Africa and Ghana respectively. The Federation reacted promptly. The salary of the National Team coach, Hodja Czorjekracj from Albania, was raised to $2,000 a week and the number of officials was doubled.

Even this did not help!

What was to be done? What could be done to keep the players?

Lightning made a last desperate effort which bordered on humiliation: the team manager took Pomerantz down to the Negev, and in the middle of the wilderness, out of range of any human ear, he made him a whispered offer of an IL3 premium for every goal scored by him.

"Score a hundred goals a month," the manager proposed, "and you've got three hundred net, tax free."

Seeing the player's blank face, the manager proposed to pay IL1.50 even for a successful penalty kick. But Pommie stood there, pale and adamant.

"Four hundred," he said. "Fixed salary!"

Without loss of time, the watch on Pomerantz was reinforced by four additional detectives. The deployment of this huge apparatus for preventing escapes was a great burden on the Federation's budget, but that venerable institution was ready for any sacrifice for the sake of a healthy sports life. And it must be admitted that only thanks to these special precautions did Pommie show up against Hapoel Kfar Maccabi on that fateful day.

The groups' actions were fully coordinated. The two tailing scouts reported by radio during the early morning hours that Mrs. Pomerantz had left the house carrying a suitcase. Within twenty minutes the Lydda Airport group discovered that a seat had been booked for a mystery passenger with a cargo of balls on the plane to Rome. What happened then is known from the daily press: the plane was confiscated. The frontiers were closed. At 1:00 p.m. the player left his home and jumped into a taxi, where two strong-arm boys were waiting for him. They hit him over the head with rubber truncheons.

Pommie regained consciousness at the football field, in his team's locker room. The coach faced him, a cocked pistol in his hand.

"You make just one suspicious move and I'll shoot you down like a mad dog," the coach said. "Now get out and play!"

Pomerantz offered only token resistance. "Come on, be a sport, pay me at least an IL7 obeying premium."

"Out!"

Pommie doubled out of the locker room with the rest of the team. The eyes of fifty thousand fans were on him. They had paid IL10 per head to see him. By then everybody knew that the Federation had asked for an injunction to prevent Pommie's leaving the country since this represented a *de facto* smuggling of capital abroad.

The rest is known to every family in Israel from the mouth of the popular sportscaster:

". . . the ball is with Pomerantz in this nineteenth minute of the game," the favorite sportscaster reported. "He passes with a marvelous feint the player appointed to guard him, runs at full speed the length of the touchline, does some brilliant dribbling and drops the two fullbacks, turns right, passes the goal line still carrying the ball, runs up the stairs of the grandstand, dodges three spectators who try to stop him, dashes past the coach, climbs the fence and jumps clear of the field—in the twenty-first minute Pomerantz has escaped!"

The audience rose to its feet, thrilled by the superb performance, but soon enough it was discovered that Pommie had after all been stopped outside. The management of Lightning-Holon had bagged him in a net they had spread out below the fence. The ball again passed into the hands of the Federation.

"Pommie, don't be a fool," the club chairman gasped as he dragged back the center forward. "We'll give you an IL5.50 haircut premium and a cheese sandwich before every game."

Complete anarchy reigned on the field. The goalkeeper of Hapoel Kfar Maccabi had taken advantage of the disturbance created by Pomerantz's break, and had tried to escape through the police gate. At the last minute he was returned in handcuffs and his club chairman tried to appease him with a onetime stay-put premium. The referee noticed what was happening and ruled a penalty shot for a violation of amateurship.

Who would kick the penalty shot?

Pommie! Pommie!

Pomerantz prepared carefully, took off and landed a mighty kick—in the ground. The ball did not even reach the goal.

What had happened? The audience wondered. This was not their Pommie! This was somebody else!

And, indeed, only now was it noticed that the player down there was short, thin and unkept, whereas Pommie was a bald giant.

This happened in the thirty-eighth minute!

The real Pomerantz had left the country's shores ten minutes earlier in a small motor boat headed in the general direction of Cyprus. The operation had been planned with an eye for detail worthy of *Rififi*. Pommie had indeed climbed the fence, but somebody else disguised as Pomerantz had jumped off it. The time he gained had enabled him to make the seashore. The plane ticket had been a decoy. The suitcase had been filled with stones. He was not even married. Today Pommie is the star of the Skymaster team in Rhodesia, he makes £630 a month net, and has a lot of chestnut-haired servant girls. And what's even more annoying, he is the co-author of the best-seller *I Was Pomerantz's Double.*

Improvements in the means of communication have broken down all partitions between man and man in our country and have also brought out a new type of city dweller: the neighbor-watcher. The show goes on uninterruptedly every night from eight o'clock until the blinds are pulled down.

Togetherness

One evening not long ago, as we sat quietly fuming over the literary supplements, there was a sudden ring at the door. The little one immediately jumped up, hurried over to me and said: "Go, open the door!"

Complying, I found the Grosses treading the doormat. Dov and Lucy Gross, a nice, middle-aged couple—in slippers. They introduced themselves and apologized for disturbing us at such a late hour.

"We're from across the street," they said. "May we come in for a moment?"

"Please . . ."

They went straight to the living room, circled the piano and stopped in front of the tea wagon.

"See?" Lucy Gross scoffed at her husband triumphantly. "It's not a sewing machine!"

"All right," Dov answered, purple in the face with anger. "You win. But on Tuesday I was right—they have no *Encyclopaedia Britannica*."

"I didn't mention any *Britannica*," Lucy flared up. "All I said was *Encyclopaedia* and that they are terrible snobs."

"It's a pity we didn't record what you actually said."

"It's indeed a pity!"

I realized that a fight was brewing, so I proposed we all sit down and settle the argument as becomes enlightened adults. Dov took off his raincoat and remained in his striped blue pajamas.

"We live just across the street," he explained and pointed toward the high-rise building, "there on the fifth floor. We've got superb field glasses, bought them last year in Hong Kong."

"Yes," I said, "the Japanese are making fantastic things."

"Maximum enlargement one to twenty!" Lucy bragged and fiddled with the curlers in her hair. "We can see the smallest detail in your flat with them. So yesterday Dubby behaved like a stubborn mule and swore that the dark object behind the piano was a sewing machine. I bet him it wasn't, since I could clearly see a flower vase on top of it. In the end I said to Dubby: 'You know what, we'll go over to them and check who's right.'"

"You did the right thing," I praised them, "otherwise there would have been no end to the argument. Any more problems?"

"Only the curtain," Dov sighed. "If you draw the flower-pattern curtain in front of your bedroom window, we can barely see your toes."

"There's a draft. Believe me, that's the only reason."

"I'm not complaining," thus Dubby. "You don't have to consider us. After all, it's your house."

Rapport had definitely been established. The little woman served salt sticks and tea.

"I'm dying to see whether the chewing gum is still there," Dov remarked, fingering the underside of the table. "Red chewing gum if I'm not mistaken."

"Nonsense," Lucy said, "it was yellow!"

"Red!"

They started fighting again. It was rather embarrassing: can't civilized people talk to each other for five minutes without quarreling? It so happened that the gum was green—they are not 100 percent reliable.

"Last night your guest stuck it there," Dov explained. "That tall, well-dressed man. When your wife went to the kitchen, he removed the gum from his mouth, looked around to see whether anyone was looking and stuck it underneath."

"How nice," the little one giggled. "You really see everything."

"We have no TV at home," Dov explained, "so we have to look for local entertainment. I hope you don't mind."

"No, of course not."

The little one served crackers and fruit.

"Better watch that man in the undershirt who cleans your windows," Dov remarked. "He uses your deodorant in the bathroom."

"You mean you can even see the bathroom?"

"Naw! Just a little bit of anyone standing under the shower."

"And what does it look like?"

"Very little action."

They also warned us of the fat baby-sitter who

comes in on the Sabbath.

"As soon as the kids fall asleep," Lucy disclosed, "she retires into your bedroom with a student in spectacles."

"How's the vision in the bedroom?"

"Not bad, only the flower-pattern curtain is a nuisance, as I told you."

"Is the light adequate?"

"To tell you the truth, not quite," Dov admitted. "Sometimes we see only your contours in the bed. And, of course, photographing is out of the question."

"The light is only for reading," I apologized. "We do a lot of reading in bed."

"I know, I know," thus Dov. "All the same, sometimes we're quite furious, if you must know."

"Dov," Lucy remonstrated with him, "why must you pick on them?"

She told us that her favorite scene was in the evening when the wife goes in to little Rena and gives her a hearty good-night kiss on her chubby bottom.

"It's a real pleasure to watch," she waxed enthusiastic. "Last Sunday we had a very nice couple from Canada, both of them are interior decorators, and they too agreed that they had hardly ever seen a more touching sight. They promised to send us a real telescope on a tripod, one to forty.

"My husband also wanted to buy one of those Japanese microphones you direct at windows," Lucy related, "but I said to Dubby, 'Let's wait until we can afford something real good.'"

"You're so right," I said. "One should never skimp on equipment."

Dubby got up and swept the crumbs from his pajamas. "We are so glad to have met you in person too,"
he said cheerfully and whispered in my ear discreetly.
"Watch your weight, old man, you've got a real
paunch."

"Thank you."

"You're welcome," Dubby said. "If I can be of
help, why shouldn't I? And if it's at all possible, the
flower-pattern curtain . . ."

"Of course."

We promised to go on seeing each other, and a
little while later a light went up in the house opposite.
Then Dubby's noble figure appeared on the lookout,
toting the Hong Kong field glasses. We waved to him,
and I think he waved us on.

"Nice people," the wife said. "So informal."

"Yes," I agreed, "we established excellent commu-
nications with them."

🌸 *Israel is a socialistic country by mistake, but its ties with capitalism are more than cordial. Therefore every year we convene a big economic conference, invite Jewish tycoons from all over the world and ask them to teach us how to sponge on them.*

Soak the Rich!

"This way, gentlemen."

The Economic Conference delegates left the office for the Encouragement of Investments in Orange Groves and continued their tour of the top floor of the Ministry of Finance. Directed by Dr. Bar-Bitzua, they entered a small room at the end of a corridor and motioned to the clerks busy there not to interrupt their work.

"Fine." Sir Isaac Wolfson surveyed the room. "What's going on here?"

"This is our Department for the Prevention of Easy Profits," Dr. Bar-Bitzua politely explained. "Everything here is computerized by the IBM system, as you can see for yourselves."

The guests' gaze caressed the sides of the big computer taking up the whole corner.

"This is where all information on attempts to get rich flows in," Dr. Bar-Bitzua continued. "The team here vigilantly follows every change of this sort in our economy."

He pulled a slip of paper from the humming teleprinter and read to the guests the latest news: " '*This—winter — too — many — umbrellas — were — bought — in — the — country — stop — umbrella — manufacturers — pocketed — big — sums — stop — immediate — intervention — imperative — over.*' The team will immediately translate this item into action," Dr. Bar-Bitzua remarked. "No later than this afternoon, instructions will go out for a twenty-three-percent rise in the duty on umbrella silk, besides which other possibilities of increasing levies in this branch will be checked."

"Stands to reason," agreed Lord Sieff. "But what happens if the umbrella manufacturers still make profits?"

"In that case, sir, we shall put out discouraging fine-weather reports. And should the provocation continue, we might even put a defense levy on rainwear—anything to avoid excessive profits in this branch."

"Good," Charles Clore, the British tycoon, remarked, "but, as a matter of fact, why are we against getting rich?"

"I'll tell you, sir," Dr. Bar-Bitzua replied confidentially. "It is in absolute contradiction to the laws of nature. There is no sign of a tendency to a perverse accumulation of money, either in the animal or in the vegetable kingdom. Only certain sectors of mankind are infected by this disease."

There certainly is something in that," Baron Edmond de Rothschild mused. "You've got to keep an eye on us!"

"We have not yet reached perfection in this field," Dr. Bar-Bitzua confessed, "but in certain progressive socialist countries, as for instance Albania, Cuba and

Outer Mongolia, the authorities have succeeded in completely eradicating the morbid tendency to quick enrichment."

"Well, there's still time," Sir Isaac consoled him. "After all, at the end of the Conference a coalition will be set up with the Left Socialists and that should do it."

At that moment a red pilot light started blinking in the Haifa area of the huge map hanging on the wall, and the computer processed the data in a matter of seconds. It seems that the Instant Yarmulke Company Limited of Kiryat Motzkin had that morning distributed twelve-percent dividends to shareholders. Simultaneously with this discovery, the particulars of the above company were checked. It had been set up about three years ago with Latin American capital, and a slip of paper in the handwriting of the Minister of Finance, attached to the statutes, specifically authorized a twelve-percent dividend out of profits.

"Formally, they are covered," Dr. Bar-Bitzua remarked, "but who would have believed that there would indeed be profits?"

A telephone call to the Ministry of Trade and Industry took care of this by permitting the free import of cheap Japanese yarmulkes.

"Ours is a flexible economic policy," thus Dr. Bar-Bitzua. "If the Kiryat Motzkin plant should go bankrupt next year, we would without hestiation ban the import of foreign yarmulkes. Because we have nothing against the plant as long as it doesn't make easy profits."

"Naturally," Lord Green agreed. "I am only surprised that the manufacturers themselves don't take this into consideration!"

"As a matter of fact, some plants are quite all right from this point of view. Take, for instance, the veteran Government corporations, which for the past thirteen years have shown an admirable restraint toward profits of any kind." Dr. Bar-Bitzua demonstrated how a special electronic device automatically wiped off any losses in the plant's balance sheet.

Suddenly the pilot light went up on the console in the hairdressing sector: *"The—hairdressers Jeannette— Gizi—Manci—and—Lili—are—earning—too—much— stop—what—a—shame—over,"* the console signaled. The tax on shampoo was raised by 130 percent and the alarm bell at the income-tax office rang three times, the code which demanded assets reports for the years 1948– 1972.

"We don't insist on the years before the War of Independence," Dr. Bar-Bitzua explained. "The trend is to limit the intervention of the state in the life of the private citizen, and to channel the liquid means of payment into short-term loans."

The teleprinter disgorged a new ribbon of paper:

Lawyer — Avigdor — Fleischhacker — 22 — National — Heroes — Street — third — floor — bought — his — wife — a — car — how — stop — bastard — over."

A posse immediately went out to trap the profit car. Another team carefully drafted a law forbidding the purchase of new cars for a period of five years by lawyers on National Heroes Street, provided they had been abroad more than twice in the above-mentioned period.

"Very nice," Sir Sigmund Warburg said, visibly satisfied. "The main thing is to strengthen the economy."

"Thank you, sir!"

The delegation left the room on its way back to the Conference.

"Great!" Sir Isaac burst out laughing after the door had closed behind him. "I must tell you, Dr. Bar-Bitzua, it was a lovely idea on your part to put on this show for us."

"I beg your pardon, sir?"

"This was a joke, wasn't it?" Sir Isaac asked.

"This way, gentlemen," Dr. Bar-Bitzua said with a wry smile.

❦ *The dollar is based on gold, the ruble on the secret police and the Israeli pound on the Arabs. That is, it is based on the fact that while the guns are roaring no one asks fiscal questions. Sometimes it happens that our neighbors temporarily suspend hostilities against us, and at such times inflation rears its ugly head. It should be noted that lately there has been no inflation in our country, we are sorry to say.*

The Nation's Tusk

When the House Council convoked an urgent meeting, it naturally was about the whitewash flaking off the southern wall. In the heat of the discussion, Mrs. Kalaniot remarked: "Now is a good time to buy elephants."

"Why?" we asked. "Why now of all times?"

"Because their price is still what it was before devaluation," Mrs. Kalaniot informed us. "IL6 per kilo, plus 72 percent purchase tax and 85 percent customs duty. If I had the money, I'd certainly buy an elephant."

We disapproved in the strongest terms. Felix Selig, making no attempt to conceal his scorn, said, "Don't be surprised if afterward the price of elephants sends the cost-of-living index spiraling upward, and empties the shopping-bag, and then there is a wage hike, and in the end we stand where we were at the beginning."

Ziegler laughed fit to die. "Buy an elephant—why, that's priceless," he guffawed. "You know, sometimes I have a feeling, folks, that you are not quite normal! An elephant! And what next? Who nowadays buys merchandise which does not come from a hard-currency area? Elephants are not dollar-linked, and any babe in arms will tell you that there is no chance of the price rising."

"And what if it does rise?" I asked. "After all, it is only worth while to buy elephants when prices are low, because that way there is the chance of a quick killing. Once they get more expensive, they are worthless, because you can't sell them, as they haven't got any chance of rising in price."

They didn't quite understand that, and we dispersed. I told the wife about the elephant.

"Buy one," she mused. "Just to be on the safe side."

I went to Mazalgovitch's pet shop and asked for an elephant.

Mazalgovitch replied without raising his eyes: "Right now I'm out of elephants."

I looked around the shop. Of course! In a dark corner, behind the parrot cage, stood a cow elephant.

"And that?" I asked Mazalgovitch.

He blushed and confessed that he was worried about the fate of his stock. "Today I sell, who knows how much I'll have to pay tomorrow?" he apologized. "I have two elephants in the customs as well and can't clear them, because the Government demands a surtax, claiming that the elephants' price will go up if a surtax is levied on them."

I left empty-handed. To tell the truth, I was not overly sorry—after all, so far I had lived without an elephant. And then what did I see on Weizmann Street?

Ziegler calmly walking in the roadway with an elephant on a leash.

"Listen," I turned on him. "Where did you get that elephant?"

"What elephant?" Ziegler asked.

"The one behind you." I pointed.

"Oh, that?" Ziegler stuttered. "It's not mine. My cousin is on reserve duty and asked me to exercise the poor beast."

That sounded fishy. Since when does one have to exercise elephants? What does he think it is, a dog?

The wife, too, thought the idea absolutely ridiculous.

"Something is going on in this house," she said. "Since yesterday I've heard trumpeting coming from Mrs. Kalaniot's apartment. She must have read that the Government is about to abolish the travel tax on pachyderms."

It is horrible to realize that everybody else is taking steps and only you are allowing events to overtake you. Also, the house had developed a noticeable list. In the night we heard muffled thuds on the staircase. We peeked out. Erna Selig and her husband were tiptoeing in with two elephants in tow.

But it was only next morning, when we opened the newspaper, that we understood the meaning of this action. An official inquiry into the circumstances of the linked tusk prices had been opened.

So the wretches were taking care of themselves! Our bedroom ceiling was sagging. The little woman had an attack of hysterics.

"Go," she shrieked, "and don't come back without

an elephant! Everybody knows how to look after himself except you!"

That very evening I got an elephant at a most reasonable price. I bought it from a new immigrant who was tax-exempt. We moved the elephant at sundown when there were fewer people on the streets. Why should they see I'm panicky, right? The elephant could hardly squeeze through the entrance, which had become much lower since the whole building lately had subsided several inches into the ground. We carefully concealed the animal on the kitchen porch. (New immigrants may not sell their elephants for at least a year, or else they pay luxury tax.) We went to bed, perhaps for the first time since devaluation, in a better mood.

"You see?" I said to the wife. "Now I'm calm."

Next morning the house collapsed. Out of the debris eleven dazed elephants extricated themselves and set off at a wild gallop toward the market. People say all this could have been avoided had they been tied to the index.

Sure, there is a little anarchy right now, but that is the price of economic independence.

❦ *Our sympathy for elephants stems from the fact that, as a small and fighting nation, we instinctively side with the underdog. This historic sympathy of ours is subject to only one reservation: the underdog must be house-trained.*

Tsvinji Pees

Tsvinji, the Curse of the Mongolian Steppes, was discovered one cold dawn in what, at the time, still qualified as my ornamental garden. It was about 5.30 A.M. and people were still a-slumber, all except politicians, who have to get up early lest the wheels stop turning. Suddenly a desperate whine filtered in through the Venetian blinds. Bleary-eyed, I raised a blind and peered out. In the middle of my now defunct ornamental garden a very small puppy was digging up the ground with his little paws and chewing up the greenery around him—toothless, but with great gusto. The puppy was very white, very young, of undetermined race, and quite incapable of coordinating the movement of its four legs. I was just about to close the blind and return to my warm blankets, but then my wife spoke up.

"What's that?"

"A puppy."

"How cute," thus the woman. "Show me."

I opened the door wide, whereupon the puppy tottered into our room and peed on the red carpet.

I don't like to have my red carpet peed on. Therefore I grabbed the puppy and removed him to the garden in the hope that He who nourishes the birds of the sky would also remove him somewhere. But the puppy turned on a shrill whine, whereupon Mrs. Toscanini rushed over to us in her dressing gown and embarked on a formal speech in favor of our adopting the little orphan. She dwelt on the well-known fact that a dog is a faithful animal, and clever too, and clean; as a matter of fact, man has no better friend in this rotten world, except the Government, maybe.

"All right," I said to Mrs. Toscanini, "if it's so desirable to keep a dog, why don't you adopt this one?"

"Do you think I've gone out of my mind?" thus Mrs. Toscanini. "Haven't I got enough troubles?"

And that's how the puppy was adopted by us. After a brief family confab, we gave him the brand-new name of Tsvinji, because of the brown spots on his ears, or perhaps for some other reason, I don't quite remember. Tsvinji quickly attained member-of-the-family status and gradually wormed himself into our hearts. In all fairness, one has to admit that he ate anything that came within range of his jaws, from radio aerials to alarm clocks; he also carried home from the neighboring gardens all sorts of little cadavers. On the other hand, the little mutt was very much attached to us and wagged his tail like a metronome whenever we called him, provided he spotted Hungarian salami in our hands. Within an amazingly brief time I taught Tsvinji a large number of commands—to quote but a few: "Down! Down!" (Tsvinji cocks his ears and licks my face) and "Jump!" (at this command Tsvinji as a rule scratches his belly) and "Paw!" (the dog does not move, plays possum). In short, Tsvinji is not one of those trained, servile dogs that obey orders mechanically, but an independent, clever, adult canine.

But he always pees on the carpet.

He always pees and only on the carpet.

Why?

We don't know. According to the basic laws of psychology, it may be assumed that this is a result of some experiences in the suckling period. In other words, Tsvinji was born in a field of red poppies, and therefore whenever he sees the red carpet for which I paid a fortune, he has got to pee or else it's the end of the world.

But, as a matter of fact, the reason is not important —the facts and the stains remain facts and stains.

Naturally, I did not resign myself to Tzvinji's curious habits, and after a few weeks I started him on a severe withdrawal regime.

"It's forbidden on the carpet! Forbidden! Phooey!" I shouted at him whenever he favored the red carpet with his attentions. On the other hand, I lavished praise and caresses on him whenever he fulfilled his needs by mistake in my ornamental garden, though under the impact of his growing teeth the garden gradually took on the look of the Gobi Desert. From all these actions of mine, Tsvinji drew the conclusion that I am a very capricious god who alternately rages and radiates happiness because of his peeing—who can understand these humans?

Personally, I had to admit that Tsvinji was simply unable to grasp the most elementary rules of hygiene and therefore I decided to break him of this childish habit gradually. My plan was that first I'd accustom him to peeing not on red, but on other carpets; then gradually I'd lure him outdoors, so that he could unburden himself there—or, even better, on neighboring land. With that aim in view, I covered the red carpet with a gray one and fixed half a bottle of cream as reward for every peeing realized on a gray field. A week later, when Tsvinji had obviously become accustomed to gray, I unveiled again the red carpet, whereupon the cur made a mad dash for it (faithfulness!) and was happier than ever before.

Then I introduced the exercise routine with the bright idea of developing a love of nature in Tsvinji's heart. I bought a strong green leash and every night walked the animal to Petach-Tikva and back. All through our walk Tsvinji gave proof of remarkable restraint, but as we approached our home he became restless and from the doorway made a beeline for the red carpet.

I understood that this was due to a complicated biological process which probably had deep roots, but occasionally the thought flashed through my mind: what did I need this for? I mentioned this to the wife and she said that she was a follower of Rousseau, the French philosopher, who had stated that anything that was natural was beautiful. In other words, it was natural that Tsvinji should always pee on our red carpet.

But what does nature do in its boundless wisdom?

One morning Mrs. Toscanini came over to donate some bones for the dog and I complained to her that the dog was all mixed up hygiene-wise.

"Because you don't know how to educate him,"

Mrs. Toscanini said. "What you have to do is this:
every time he wets the red carpet, rub his nose in the
puddle, slap his rump and toss him out the window.
That's how it's done."

That's what I did, though I'm not an advocate of
corporal punishment. Tsvinji came, did, I rubbed his
nose, slapped him and tossed him out of the window.
Breaking Tsvinji's habit had become my life's vocation.
If the process had to be repeated three times, I repeated
it three times. And slowly, gradually, I achieved some results. Nowadays Tsvinji no longer behaves as of old.
Something of my training has stuck. True, he still pees
only on the red carpet, but afterward he jumps out of
the window all by himself without any assistance on my
part. Then he waits outside for me to come and praise
him.

🌷 *We also have great sympathy for the undercat, because if the dog is man's best friend, the Jewish cat is his best employer.*

A Bottle for Pussy

We all have our weaknesses. Some of us drink or gamble, others chase skirts or trousers or are ministers of finance. My wife, for instance, chases pussy-cats. But not those pampered masses of fluff that purr under the caressing hand like an amorous electric razor—she specializes in those miserable little creatures that miaow, abandoned, at street corners. As soon as my wife spots one of these poor things, her heart breaks, she sheds a few tears, brings the little orphan home, and cares for it with great devotion and love until the next morning, when she gets bored with it. It is then that my wife says to her husband:

"Why don't you do something around this house! I can't do everything by myself!"

That's how it went with Pussy as well.

The wife discovered the above kitten one morning at the corner of 29 November Street. It was black and lean, but frolicked about in the sand. However, as soon as it spotted my spouse approaching, it immediately turned on its side and gave her to understand with heart-rending miaowing that it was ready for adoption. My wife's heart was duly rent—tears, etc. Pussy was hauled home and we put a plateful of sweetened milk in front of her, but she didn't even touch it. She sniffed at it, but that was all.

The wife almost collapsed. Without food, the kitten's hours were numbered. Something had to be done at once. Somehow we hit upon the life-saving idea that since Pussy belonged to the large and happy family of mammals, she should be fed from a bottle.

"Splendid," I said. "It so happens that our last-born, Amir, has about eighty permanently sterilized bottles."

"Oh yeah?" the woman flared up. "You expect me to feed a cat from Amireleh's bottle? Go to the pharmacy at once and buy a bottle for Pussy."

"Oh no, I won't," I answered, "I am ashamed."

It was a rather embarrassing situation. How can an adult, well-established male go to a pharmacy and say "Give me a bottle for cats"? It would sound very odd indeed. I decided therefore to keep the bottle's real use a secret.

"Shalom," I said therefore to the friendly neighborhood pharmacist, "I'd like a bottle."

"How is Amir?" she asked.

"Thank you, he's over twelve pounds now."

"Splendid, what kind of bottle would you like?"

"The cheapest."

An ominous silence descended. The other customers drew away from me and watched me from below half-lowered eyelids. "Just look at him," their glances said, "a well-dressed man, with glasses, drives a big car —but for his little son he buys the cheapest bottle. Shocking, really shocking."

The smile had vanished from the pharmacist's

face. "As you like," she said, "but it is my duty to warn you that these cheap bottles break very easily."

"Never mind," I muttered, "we'll glue it together."

The pharmacist shrugged and placed before me an assortment of bottles, from marvelous Made-in-Great-Britain jumbo bottles down to a little brown flask which was an abomination.

"That's it," I said, blushing, "give me the brown one."

Then, quite unexpectedly, a plump lady standing next to me intervened. "I have no right to stick my nose into your private affairs, sir, yet I would like to ask you to think again before you act. Man has no greater treasure than his children! If you are so hard-pressed and must save, do it on anything else, but don't begrudge your little son the best! Take the word of an experienced mother!"

She was very fat and I didn't like her. I asked what were the prices. The big wonder bottles cost from IL15 to IL18.50 while the little brown one cost IL2.

"The kid smashes everything anyway," I stuttered. "It's not worthwhile to buy him anything expensive."

"Why should he smash everything?" the pharmacist asked. "If you support his little head with the fingers of your left hand this way, you see, sir, nothing would ever get smashed."

Before my mind's eye there appeared Pussy nicely done up in diapers, reclining on my left arm.

"I'm convinced you don't feed the kid properly," the chubby mother opined. "There is no reason why he should kick with his little legs. Have you got a nurse for the baby?"

"No . . . that is . . ."

"I'll send you one!" the corpulent mama decided. "Nothing makes more trouble than a nervous child. Just a second, it so happens that I've got the phone number on me." With that, my benefactress dialed Miriam Kussevitsky, the graduate children's nurse.

The door was only about three yards away from me. If those two burly men had not blocked my way, I would have made a dash for it and disappeared howling in the midday fog. Idle dream.

"You should really be grateful to the lady," the pharmacist encouraged me. "She's got four kids, all of them quiet, healthy darlings. Rest assured, she'll send you an expert nurse who will quickly cure Amireleh of his tantrums."

Amir is, by the way, the quietest kid in the Middle East; it is almost embarrassing the way he lies all day long on his back, not caring about what goes on around him.

My last hope was that the Kussevitsky wouldn't be home, but she was.

"The nurse is ready to come to your home tomorrow to talk things over," Fat Mama whispered triumphantly. "Would eleven A.M. suit you?"

"No," I answered, "we're busy."

"And one o'clock?"

"I have a fencing lesson."

"And your wife?"

"She too."

"Two o'clock?"

"We'll be asleep by then."

"Four o'clock?"

"Still asleep."

"Six o'clock?"

"We're expecting guests."

"Eight o'clock?"

"Museum."

"My dear, sir!" The fat lady flared up red in the face. "Her first visit won't cost you anything, if that's what's bothering you!"

The pharmacy customers were in a lynching mood. They closed around me in a hostile cordon, their behavior saying: "Why do they let such monsters have babies?" Chubby Ma smashed down the receiver and would not talk to me any more. The pharmacist asked me in an icy voice: "So should I wrap up the cheapest?"

I nodded my head wordlessly. "If only I get out of this alive," I vowed, "I'll open an orphanage for abandoned kittens."

The pharmacist threw me a glance filled with hatred and made a last attempt to awaken within me a spark of decency. "Look at this rubber nipple," she said. "It's of such poor quality that the hole very quickly widens and the child could, God forbid, choke on his food."

The blood rushed to my head, and I no longer knew or cared what I was saying.

"Never mind," I threw at her, "we'll make another child!"

That was too much! A middle-aged, distinguished gentleman stepped up to me and grabbed my lapels. "I don't know who you are or what you are, my dear sir!" he shouted. "But I would like to ask you only one question: do you realize that with these cheap bottles one feeds only cats, not babies?"

"So be it," I groaned. "Give me the best bottle."

"Eighteen-fifty," the pharmacist cooed and the mood mellowed. I became the owner of a so-called "super pyrex" baby bottle with detailed feeding charts on its side and a two-year guarantee. Fire-, water- and earthquake-proof.

The wife got a rude shock when she saw it. "What for?" she raged. "Why did you have to buy the most expensive bottle?"

"Woman," I answered. "I am ready to economize on anything except on cats!"

❧ To round out this trilogy on domestic animals, let's consider favorably the winged gramophone: the parrot. In our country the local variety receives lessons in diction by telephone, with the participation of a whole airline, strange as this may seem.

Crossed Lines

Something most upsetting happened to me the other day: in the morning I went to the office of one of the big airlines and talked to the booking clerk. I forget her name, but she had a very young face and was wearing her gray hair in a pony-tail, and she asked me in front of the glass door to leave my address with her and then I definitely remember pulling out of my pocket the wallet with the calling cards, and only when I came home did I notice that all my notes with the telephone numbers on them had fallen out, seems that the catch which holds the pages together had broken, they were square pieces of paper with a perforation on the side, most annoying . . .

I telephoned the airline. A female voice came on.

"Airline. Good morning."

"Good morning, miss," I said to her. "The other day in the morning I was in your office and talked to the booking clerk. I don't remember her name, but she has a very young face and wears her gray hair in a pony-tail, and she asked me in front of the glass door to leave my address with her, and then I remember taking the wallet out of my pocket, and only when I came home did I notice that all my notes had fallen out—"

"Just a second, sir," the girl said. "I'm only the operator, I'll switch you over to the Secretary.

"Thank you."

"Hello," a man's voice said after a few seconds, "this is the Secretary."

"It's like this, sir," I said to him. "I was in your booking office yesterday and talked to one of the clerks, I don't remember her name, but she's got a very young face and wears her gray hair in a pony-tail, and she asked me, if I'm not mistaken in front of the glass door, to leave my address with her, and I remember definitely that I then took the wallet out of my pocket and only when I came home did I notice that all my notes with the telephone numbers on them had dropped out of my wallet, seems the little catch which holds the pages together broke . . ."

"Quite," the Secretary said, "I'll put you through at once to Bookings."

There I was in an instant.

"Hello," a female voice said. "Bookings, shalom."

"Shalom," I said. "I don't know whether it's to you I talked, miss. Anyway, I spoke to one of the clerks who has a very young face and wears her gray hair in a pony-tail. Is that you?"

"No, but maybe I can help you all the same."

"Thank you," I said. "You see, that clerk asked me in front of the glass door to leave her my address and I definitely remember that I then pulled the wallet out of my pocket and only when I returned home did I notice that all the pages had fallen out of my note book . . ."

"When did that happen?"

"Day before yesterday, in the morning, miss."

"Sorry, but I wasn't on duty day before yesterday, sir. You'll have to speak to Alisa. Please hold on."

There was a brief silence, then a woman came on the line. "Good morning."

"Good morning, miss," I said. "I was in your office the other day and talked to a clerk, I don't remember her name, but she's got a very young face and wears her gray hair in a pony-tail, and she asked me in front of the glass door . . ."

"Just a second, sir," the girl said at this juncture. "This is the telephone operator again. I had you once before this morning, hadn't I? Who would you like to speak to?"

"To Alisa."

"At once! Alisa? Somebody's looking for you. Go ahead."

"Shalom, miss," I said to Alisa. "They sent me to you about those pages. That is, I was in your booking office in the morning and talked to one of the girls, I don't remember her name, but she's got a very young face and wears her gray hair in a pony-tail, and she asked me in front of the glass door to leave my address with her, and I definitely remember that I pulled the wallet out of my pocket and only when I came home . . ."

"Excuse me, sir, which Alisa are you looking for? Alisa from Air Freight, or Alisa from Bookings?"

"From Bookings."

"Well, this is not her. I'll shoot you back to the operator."

"Hello," Switchboard fluted, "shalom."

"Shalom," I said. "Give me Alisa from Bookings."

Click-click.

"Miss Alisa from Bookings?"

"Yes."

"At last!" I said to her. "I've got a problem, but I'm not sure whether this is your department."

"Tell me, sir, then we'll know."

"Look, I was in your office day before yesterday and talked to one of your clerks, I don't remember her name, but she has a very young face and wears her gray hair in a pony-tail, and she asked me in front of the glass door to leave my address with her, and I pulled out my wallet and only at home I noticed that all my notes with the telephone numbers on them had fallen out, seems the catch . . ."

"No, no," Alisa interrupted me, "I can see this is not my department. Have you spoken to the Secretary?"

"Yes, to a man down there."

"To Stern?"

"He didn't sound like Stern."

"All right, I'll put you through to Stern."

She asked the operator to put me through to Stern.

"Good evening," Stern said. "Stern."

"Did I speak to you about six hours ago, sir?"

"About what?"

"About my having been in your booking office the day before yesterday in the morning and losing a few pages of notes."

"No, it must have been somebody else, sir. But what exactly happened?"

"Well, you see, I talked in the booking office with

one of the clerks, I don't remember her name, but she's got a very young face and wears her gray hair in a pony-tail, and if I'm not mistaken she asked me in front of the glass door . . ."

"Excuse me, there's a terrible racket here, I can hardly hear you," Stern interrupted me. "I'll go over to my room, hang on."

A very short while later he called me from his room.

"Hello," Stern said. "This is better. So I understand that you called at the booking office . . ."

"Yes, in the morning," I said to him. "I talked there to one of the clerks, I don't know her name, but she has a very young face and wears her hair in a pony-tail, and she asked me in front of the glass door for my address, and then I definitely remember taking out my wallet and only when I came home did I notice that all the pages had fallen out of the notebook . . ."

"What happened?"

"Seems the catch which holds the pages together broke."

"These things happen," Stern remarked. "So I assume those pages ought to be somewhere around here. Why don't you let me ask the boys?"

I could hear his muffled voice through the receiver telling his colleagues in the other room that someone had been here the other day and talked to one of the girls with a young face and her gray hair tied up in a pony, it must have been Stella, and she asked for his address and then he pulled out his wallet, and when he came home the notebook was gone, with all those pages of important telephone numbers . . .

"Just a second," I heard somebody's voice, "I think the janitor said something yesterday about finding a notebook."

In a moment they put me through to the janitor.

"Were they square pages, perforated on the side?" the janitor asked.

"That's right," I said. "With telephone numbers on them."

"Well, I sent them yesterday to your address. You should get them in today's mail."

"Thank you."

"As a matter of fact, what happened?"

"Simply this," I said to the janitor. "The other day I was in your booking office and talked to one of the girls, I don't remember her name, but she had a very young face and wore her gray hair in a pony-tail, and in front of the glass door she asked me for my address, and I pulled the wallet out of my pocket, and when I came home I noticed that the notebook with all the telephone numbers was gone, the catch which holds the pages together must have broken . . ."

"Well, what really matters is that we found it. Good night, sir."

"Good night."

*♣ Since our Government sees in peace a precondition
for peace, it cannot waive a dialogue between the parties
as a well-tested means of communication. Naturally, our
neighbors cannot agree to this demand, which borders
on blackmail, as it would create the impression that they
had been defeated in war by a state which actually exists.*

Birth Pangs

In these historic times when the solution to our
regional crisis is just around the next corner of the U.N.
lobby, this writer thinks it only fit to sum up for poster-
ity the history of Dr. Gunnar Jarring's mission.

It will be remembered that our Government had
expressed right from the beginning the view that results
could be achieved only by having the parties meet face
to face. Egypt immediately countered that it would not
accept any invitation in which the word "table" was
mentioned, while Jordan demanded that the expression
"meeting" be changed to the more general "gathering."

After repeated visits by Dr. Jarring to Cairo, the
Egyptian Government somewhat softened its stand and
gave its consent to an official formula according to
which the parties would be "secluded" somewhere, but
stipulated that the seclusion would not take place in
the same room with the representatives of the Tel Aviv
Government.

The Israeli Government proposed that the two
delegations be put up in two adjacent rooms and the

partition between them be torn down once the negotiations started.

Egypt replied to Dr. Jarring that the partition was imperative, while Israel continued to demand that the delegations sit around the same table. The negotiations almost reached an impasse when Dr. Jarring came up with a compromise according to which the parties would sit in separate rooms but around the same table —that is, a special team of U.N. porters would move the common table from room to room, according to who had the floor.

The Egyptian reply was brief: *We won't sit with them.*

The Israeli proposal: *Negotiate standing.*

Jordan: *Walking.*

Egypt torpedoed the plan by declaring that it was willing to negotiate only with Dr. Jarring, and here a very interesting phase in the history of the contacts between the parties was started. What happened was that the Israeli Government officially notified the U.N. Secretariat that a Tel Aviv Ear, Nose and Throat Specialist by the name of Dr. Jarring was willing to carry on direct negotiations with the Egyptian Government. For a while it looked as if Cairo was going to accept this face-saving device, but then it was learned that the Israeli Dr. Jarring was not a Gunnar but only a Simon, and the scheme fell through.

At this stage the Jordanians proposed that, to avoid direct negotiations, the parties should sit with their profiles to each other, this way hardly seeing their counterparts. But Israel insisted on the face-to-face formula, and Dr. Jarring came up with a new device: the delegations would sit facing each other but, instead of talking among themselves, would communicate through previously agreed-upon signals, such as:

Raised hand, four extended fingers, bent thumb: *retreat!*

Thumb inserted between index and middle finger, clenched fist: *Oh yeah!*

Clenched fist, raised index: *May I leave the room?*

The Jordanian Government unofficially agreed, on condition that the signs be in English, but Cairo again voiced reservations regarding any kind of face-to-face talks. Dr. Jarring tried to persuade the Israeli Government to make a gesture of goodwill to break the stalemate and proposed that the parties should converse face-to-face with a glass plate separating them and conversation be through lip-reading. The Egyptians demanded a glass plate at least 12 millimeters thick, while the Hashemite Kingdom contented itself with 8.5 millimeters and earned praise for its moderation in the American press.

At this point the Israeli Government refused to play ball and insisted that only absolutely direct talks were feasible. Dr. Jarring took to Cairo a new plan, according to which the talks would be direct between the delegations but they would talk into a tape-recorder that would be passed from hand to hand at conversation speed. Egypt agreed, on condition that the tape-recorder be Dr. Jarring's private property, whereas Israel voiced its opposition, for in this case the tape-recorder would be simply a mediator and, as such, was out. At this stage the Jordanian Government proposed that the talks be started through the medium of well-trained parrots, but took back the proposal under Egyptian pressure and instead proposed the unconditional-retreat solution, a compromise which was rejected by the Israeli Government as insufficient at the present stage.

Contacts continue.

In TV Westerns there is always a bad guy who shoots the good guy in the back. In the Oriental Western of our area, the good guy refused to cooperate and be shot in the back, and ever since he has been the bad guy and that is very good. Even in British TV.

Good Guys, Bad Guys

If you are a TV man, a friend of our area and in addition thoroughly British, it is quite superfluous, really, to remind you of one of your noble nation's basic tenets: Never take sides! However tempting, and even camp, it may be to champion the underdog, in the sportive spirit so characteristic of your country, you may not openly support Egypt, Jordan, Iraq, Syria, Saudia Arabia, Kuweit, Algiers, Morocco, Libya, Sudan or Southern Yemen. Your task is to show the British viewer the bare facts only and leave the conclusions to his personal judgment. It is therefore imperative that you shoot your movie on both sides of the armistice line, without prejudice, inspired by an ardent desire for true information, without editorializing, but skillfully exploiting the opportunities of dynamic analysis.

Here, for example, is a very appropriate opening to the Mediterranean drama unfolding before our eyes: a dozen or so tattered tents in the heart of the desert, a blinding sandstorm, here and there a few mangy jackals. An old Arab staggers about among the tents with his little granddaughter. The child cries. The pathetic couple stop in front of the camera, look into it for an agonizingly long while with their sad eyes and don't say anything.

Cut.

A house in Savyon, Israel. In a beautiful garden, on a luxuriantly verdant lawn, chubby, well-dressed Jewish children frolic, their laughter resounding all over the villa suburb. You may also film the children cowering in the shelters of the shelled villages, but that of course would be less impressive, since in that case there would be no contrast between the two rival sides.

Because contrast is one of the most effective cinematic means, it poignantly emphasizes the difference between the contestants without taking sides in any way whatsoever. For instance: A Bedouin caravan passes over the desert horizon—some emaciated camels, a miniaturized donkey. They are few, scared, quiet. To balance them you may show, for instance, the Tel Aviv football stadium in the second half of the game. Contrast. On the one side, a scabby Arab dog scavenging on a refuse dump; on the other side, the National Dog Show in Ramat Gan with a close-up of the winner, a huge black boxer.

Always be scrupulously impartial.

It is said that Arab children are most photogenic; it would be a good idea to give them a few reels. And on the Israeli side don't neglect the soldiers. It shouldn't be too difficult to shoot their hob-nailed boots as they march along, practically goose-stepping. Most effective, old boy, most effective. From there you may cut back to the Arab children, wallowing in the mud, *Angst* in their eyes. In a demolished terrorist base, say. Ruins. Rickety huts. A skinny cat crosses the torn-up road. Palls of smoke in the background. Cut.

A military cemetery with tombstones of hundreds of Jewish boys killed at the start of their lives; bereaved parents who will never find consolation for their loss. That isn't bad, but there is an even better shot: a fat, bespectacled Tel Aviv citizen gorging himself on chocolate cake. Yes, on second thought, Fatso is the right solution. Naturally, it is not a must that the citizen in question be fat and bespectacled. But since the terrorist cat was skinny and without spectacles, this helps to bring out the contrast. The fat, bespectacled Tel Aviv citizen sits in the parlor of his apartment and answers questions while puffing on his filter cigarette. On the walls oil paintings, in the background a nice woman in a mini.

We ask the bespectacled fat man: "Do you believe sir, that retaliatory actions achieve anything?"

"Definitely," answers Fatso. "It's a fact that after each such action the number of sabotage acts drops. True, retaliation is alien to Jewish tradition and our fervent wish for peace with our neighbors, but when the lives of my children are at stake—I can't afford to be squeamish about my methods."

An excellent reply, but, alas, too long. A responsible TV man must consider the time element. So part of the answer has to be cut. Only the essence is left:

"It is alien to Jewish tradition," or "After such action the number of sabotage acts drops," or perhaps "I can't afford to be squeamish about my methods, sir." Yes, the last one is the best—brief and to the point. "Do you believe sir, that retaliatory action achieves anything?" "I can't afford to be squeamish about my methods, sir." Concise, certainly.

Briefness is a very important point. Answers have to be properly filtered and weeded. Take, for instance, the following dialogue with the bespectacled fellow in his parlor:

"Do you realize, sir, that you are killing dozens of innocent people by shelling Arab villages?"

"This is most unfortunate, but we never start those shellings."

"And what about the humanitarian aspect?"

"As for that, we won't be preached at by the representatives of a people who in the last world war killed off hundreds of thousands of civilians through carpet-bombing air raids."

"How can you compare the Arabs with the Nazis?"

"Indeed, there is no comparison. The Germans never proclaimed any intention of destroying Britain with all its inhabitants. You are right, there is no similarity."

That, for instance, is an excellent conversation, factual but long, long, long. It is doubtful that it could be squeezed into a program lasting a bare hour. Instead, one can give a few brief sentences by an anonymous freedom-fighter in his training camp. The Fatah man is a stocky young fellow with blue eyes, his hair tousled by the desert wind.

"This is my land," he says succinctly. "I was born here, here my father was born, my grandfather, my whole family. The Jews chased us away, robbed us of our lands. They don't want peace, they want war. We have no choice but to fight."

At this juncture, bow your head, British TV man, and plug up your ears. In your stead, bespectacled Fatso answers from his comfortable armchair: "We could have captured Cairo!" Quite possibly the Fatah man had added another sentence or two about rumors regarding a certain tendency to push the Jews into the sea, but that's—how shall we put it?—hoary old stuff, really.

Arab fighters in training. They are few and lonely. They have no money or arms. But their spirit is unbroken. They fight for the liberation of their fatherland. Cut.

Israeli soldiers in full battle equipment carry out a search in a small Arab village. They scatter household goods all over the place. A little kid is crying. At nightfall Fatah fighters go out toward the border. On their backs canisters of explosives. Silence. They disappear, crawling. Suddenly—boom! A tremendous explosion, the sky is colored red! The Jews have blown up a house in which one of the saboteurs was hiding. A small kid cries. An Israeli helicopter lands, a military march, the Independence Day parade in conquered Jerusalem . . .

The program winds up with a worried and haggard look on your face:

"So there is no solution to the historic drama. As long as the two sides stubbornly refuse to sit down at the negotiating table, the Middle East remains a powder keg endangering world peace . . ."

Time permitting, we may have a glance at the tin huts of the refugee camps. Afterward the Israel Philharmonic Auditorium. The barren wilderness. Jewish oil sheiks. A little Arab kid cries and chews a crust of dry bread. End.

One of the most resounding victories of the Arab states is the U.N. Security Council, which in the past twenty years has not found it necessary to censure them even once. The Security Council's censure is reserved exclusively for our aggressive state. As a matter of fact, we have become so accustomed to the weekly censure that its absence creates in us a feeling of void. After all, we took out a subscription, didn't we?

Victory in Council

The Pakistan draft resolution censuring Israel for the invasion of Czechoslovakia by the Red Army was submitted in the early hours of the day before yesterday to this month's Chairman of the Security Council, and ever since then negotiations have been underway between the various delegations, aiming at an agreed-on stance. It was found during the behind-the-scenes talks that the majority required for a censure vote would be hard to attain, since only eight states were unreservedly supporting it: Poland, the Soviet Union, Nigeria, Algiers, Yugoslavia, Saudi Arabia, White Russia and the sponsor of the resolution, Pakistan. According to rumor, the U.S. was having certain reservations about placing the entire blame on Israel, while Belgium and Canada had asked for a postponement of the deliberations so that a compromise acceptable to all the parties could be worked out.

Before the meeting was postponed by a minute majority, Ambassador Joseph Tekoah succeeded in clarifying to the full Council the Israeli Government's stand. "It is not Israel which invaded the territory of the Czech Socialist Republic, but Russia," the Israel delegate said, "so it's Russia which should be censured and not us!"

Jacob Malik, the Soviet delegate, left the hall ostentatiously, shouting at Tekoah, his face contorted with rage: "For once, Goebbels' methods won't help you! You're playing with fire!"

At this point, it will be remembered, the Turkish Chairman interrupted Mr. Tekoah so as to make possible further behind-the-scenes talks. From the secret reports it was found that Nicaragua, Belgium and Canada were showing limited understanding of the Israeli position regarding the nature of the occupation regime in Czechoslovakia; on the other hand, the Belgian representative explained in a confidential chat with the Israeli delegation that there was no sense in championing a stand which had no chance at all of getting the necessary votes. "After all," he pointed out, "we are not a bunch of kids." The French representative expressed his disapproval of the fact that no U.N. observer had been on the spot in Czechoslovakia to report on the course of events there, then asked for guidance from Paris.

In sharp contrast was the American delegation's demonstration of sympathy and moderation. "Perhaps it would indeed have been more justified to censure the Soviet Union," the head of the U.S. delegation admitted in private conversation, "but the Russians have the veto right in Council, as you know. Developments here should be regarded as part of United States global strat-

egy aimed at safeguarding the prestige of U.N. institutions at all costs." Tekoah pointed out that the U.S.
had just as much right to cast a veto as the Soviet
Union, but the American representative indignantly rejected any comparison with "those hoodlums."

The atmosphere in the lobbies became very tense
after the Algerians distributed a venomous pamphlet
calling Israel "blackmailers," and Pravda renewed its
attacks against the "Nazi cohorts of Tel Aviv reeling
with the drunkenness of conquest."

The Israeli delegation did not remain idle, but submitted to the Secretariat authentic photos showing
Russian armored cars cruising on the streets of Prague.
However, the American representative furiously demanded the prompt withdrawal of the photos "showing
hoary old facts which make no contribution toward a
clarification of the situation." Behind-the-scenes talks
reached a critical stage: Yugoslavia and Nigeria drafted
a new censure motion in which Nigeria accused Israel
of genocide, but when it was found that the securing of
nine votes was doubtful, the two states contented
themselves with a joint declaration with Saudi Arabia in
which Israel was termed a "neo-fascist slave trader,
murderer of the Czech people."

The U.S. head delegate sent a tranquilizing personal note to the Israelis: "Don't react! We're acting in
the background."

And indeed the energetic stance of our overseas sister had the expected effect and at the last moment the
Soviet Union withdrew its outspoken censure motion,
in exchange for a Western promise of unanimous support for the amended Polish formula reading as follows:

"The Security Council expresses its regret for the act of aggression in Eastern Europe. The Council warns Israel against any future deviation from the principles of the United Nations." Before the Council adjourned, the following amendment authored by White Russia was added to the resolution: *"Furthermore, Israel is to desist from causing further earthquakes in Iran,"* but all this does not detract from the fact that no sanctions were so much as mentioned in the final draft, and, as pointed out by Foreign Ministry circles in Jerusalem, "the Council resolution does not *directly* connect the events in Czechoslovakia with Israel's name, since the two relevant clauses are separated by a full stop." Attention was also drawn to the word "causing" in connection with earthquakes in Iran, a term which does *not* express an open accusation regarding malicious intentions on Israel's part and does not rule out the possibility of a mere coincidence. And last but not least, it should be noted that the Council expressed its "regret," but not "deep regret," and here the moderating influence of the American delegation is clearly felt.

"The draft resolution censuring Israel for the occupation of Czechoslovakia failed dismally," the Foreign Minister summed up the achievements of his delegation at the United Nations before the Cabinet. "This diplomatic victory is due to three factors: (a) an all-embracing information campaign; (b) the solid support of a friendly power; (c) justice."

🌺 *The much-desired peace in our area will not be brought about by the Four Powers or by the U.N. Secretary General, but by the sexy announcer of Jordanian TV, who incites against us in such a charming manner that one would like to kiss and hug her. If only the dimples of the Cairo announcer could be seen more clearly on our screens, we would quickly integrate into the Arab Liberation Movement.*

The Channel 5 Panacea

We bought a TV set for the child.

When we visited the Geigers, just a few houses away from us, their new set had been caterwauling with some awful Arab choir. My little wife had seated Amir on her knees in front of the screen and had succeeded in pushing two whole sandwiches into his gaping mouth, an unprecedented achievement for this inveterate hunger striker.

"Well, Amir," the enthusiastic wife asked, "would you like Daddy to buy you a TV set?"

"No," Amir answered, "I want a bicycle."

No snotty brat is going to tell me what to buy or not to buy! Bicycles are quite useless for stuffing purposes; on the contrary, the kid would only ride it for hours in the back yard and it would be a man's job to lure him back in. It is a fact that there is Educational TV, but who ever heard of educational bicycles? So we bought a TV set for the child. We chose the most advanced model on the market, with a lot of knobs and buttons and even more monthly installments, and also inquired about an adequate antenna.

"Listen," I said to the technician, "I don't want to receive those Arab horrors, only Israel!"

"So all you'll need is a small room antenna with a single arm," the technician answered. "So help me, you're right, sir!"

I ordered a twenty-yard roof antenna with five arms. Who knows? One day we might capture Cairo and then I want to be able to receive their educational broadcasts for the kid. But in the meantime we have to make do with Israel's experimental programs. These are excellent programs indeed—the only problem is that they are rather brief. On the evening when we inaugurated the set, for instance, they gave a scene from a live play, but unfortunately just then a telegram arrived, and by the time I had signed the receipt, the broadcast was over. So we tried to get some Arab station on Channel 5 just to test the roof antenna for the kid, and on the screen there appeared a dark-skinned broad who shrilled on and on in her mother tongue. This writer, because of his overseas origin, is not familiar with the area's leading language, but the little woman, a born sabra, listened raptly to the end and then reported: "I didn't understand a word. She spoke literary Arabic."

Then we got a well-dressed, cross-eyed gentleman who wept, accompanied by a colossal string orchestra. They repeated the same tune over and over again, with the singer modulating his mewing voice in the most ridiculous curlicues. "Good Lord," I mused, "what am I doing here, an intellectual imbued with European culture, wasting my precious time on squealing aborigines?" Half an hour later I tore myself away from the endless sing-song and did not return to the wearisome set until the newscast. Only then did we realize that we had captured Amman, strongpoint of the Hashemite Kingdom. We knew this because the mustachioed and somewhat cross-eyed announcer first of all sent best wishes in his guttural voice to King Hussein recovering from a slight cold. The announcer also addressed us, because he repeated several times the word "Yezrailin" and his eyes sprewed fire as he looked me straight in the face, or maybe he looked at somebody behind me, it was hard to say.

"Woman," I asked, "what's he saying?"

"Don't know," the wife translated. "He is speaking literary Arabic, don't interrupt!"

And for that she had to sit moon-struck for a whole evening in front of the set! Perhaps the overstuffed over-comfortable armchairs were to blame. In any case, I almost fell asleep in the middle of the burlesque broadcast after the news. Never in my life had I seen anything as primitive and boring: a man was dressed like a woman and another wore pajamas and his wife arrived home and then the disguised man said something and the one in pajamas shouted at the man who had come with his wife and then both of them, the one with the wife and the other, went somewhere and a fat lady came and shouted something to the disguised man and then the pajamaed man started running in circles and cursed her and then the two who had gone came back and shouted at the fat woman and she said something and then the dressed-up man fled and bumped into the one who was just coming in with the wife of the pajamaed fellow and things like that . . .

How long can one watch such a "show"? After two and a half hours I felt terribly tired and was deeply grateful to the station for releasing me from this nightmare with the Jordanian Anthem and the life-sized portrait of King Hussein. It was rather late by the time we went to bed that night, and in my dream I heard all the time the guttural ornamentations of the elegant singer and briefly chased the dark-haired girl announcer and kept shouting: "Abadan, Abadan!" I don't know why, since I don't even know such a word.

The next day I tuned in experimentally, just to show the dark-haired announcer to the kid, but it so happened that a chestnut-haired one had taken over, and she was much less convincing and a little cross-eyed. She also talked a great deal and was followed by a young singer, quite a nice girl called Nadia, who sang anti-Israeli lullabies—that is, she stood in front of a piece of colored cardboard and every time she intoned, "Inshallah, kill them all!" about a dozen men crouching in front of her in a crescent, answered: "Kill them all! Kill them all!"

Admittedly the text was rather naïve, but the melody pleasant. I sank deep in my armchair and, sucking on a succession of menthol candies, tried not to drop off again. But my eyelids suddenly became leaden and my jaw went to sleep or something, and all of a sudden I discovered that I was sitting with my mouth agape and, according to my wife, I had even hummed the refrain: "Kill them all!"

"I'm humming? Who's humming?" I sneered at

the woman from the armchair. "Dashrini, ya hamra!" which is Arabic for "shut up!"

By the way, the Arab stations come on at 9:00 A.M. The next day, for instance, we saw Jordanian Prime Minister el-Talhouni addressing trade-union activists or something. He is a handsome fellow, Talhouni, pleasantly cross-eyed and with a marvelous guttural voice. He talked for about an hour and a half against our enemies —that is, against us—and every time he said "Falastin biladna, vaal Yahud kiladna!"—i.e., "Palestine is ours, death to the Jews!"—we enthusiastically applauded. But after a while he became boring and I sighed with relief when a new orchestra appeared and started playing a soothing tune. It should be noted that every single one of these violinists is an artist in his own right. They keep a sort of wonderful inner beat, which possibly sounds monotonous to people without antennas, but for sleeping it is ideal. To tell the truth, I felt all the time a very pleasant weariness, and my jaw again fell open and my tongue became twisted and my eyes half closed, so that I hardly noticed the wife standing in front of me, mute fear on her face.

"Ephraim," she whispered, "what are you doing?"

"Well, what am I doing?" I was holding a pearl necklace and running the pearls between my fingers one by one—I couldn't tell you why even if you killed me. I couldn't remember when I had torn it off her neck. I was also humming gutturally. And getting fat. During Gamal Abdel Nasser's speech the other day I consumed, if memory serves me, a pailful of hummus and burgul and a basketful of pistachio nuts. I enjoyed the speech—I love that Nasser as if he were my own brother. He is very good-looking. I waited for our Nadia, for the kid's sake, but the chestnut-haired girl announced a wonderful farce with the participation of the boys. It was excruciatingly funny.

"Yah, woman," I said to the wife, "shlabi ktir!"

"Aiuah!"

She has become slightly cross-eyed, the little one, but it really doesn't bother me. We are a great deal together lately, me and my spouse. True, she yelled at me the other day when I upset my water pipe on the carpet, but what matters is that the wife is quite good at backgammon. Yesterday she beat me three times running while some stupid American thriller was being shown on Channel 5. At night we recite together the best of the Amman publicity jingles for the kid: "Hey, Pepsi!" and "Rim Cigarettes." I also laid on Turkish slippers and lots of pillows and halva and mutton. I am only sorry that because of my strong European background I cannot become better assimilated in the area. But, Allah willing, I hope that soon الذي نسعى اليه العيش الايجابية ، وخلق المجتمع المنسجم if I am not mistaken.

❦ *In Jewish marriages, a central and honored part is assigned to the woman as mother to her children and mother to her husband. The good Jewish husband as a rule says to himself before taking any fateful decision: "I'll ask the little woman first." And he always asks and the little woman sometimes even answers him. The husband's complaints are registered in the "From the Mouths of Babes" column.*

What to Buy Teacher?

I am lying on my couch, fully dressed. Over my head the lamp burns brightly, the morning papers are underfoot. In my head wild thoughts chase each other. The little woman crouches before the mirror at the end of the room, smearing on her face Bio-Placenta Cream, which miraculously refreshes the cells of the skin. It is the hour of truth for artists of my age. For a number of weeks now I have been troubled by a cruel dilemma. I can no longer keep quiet, I must share with somebody the decisions which will shape my fate for the coming decade. After all, this is what a man is married for, isn't it?

"Darling," I say in a choking voice, "I must tell you something, and please don't get alarmed or draw hasty conclusions. For quite a while now I have increasingly felt that I have reached my zenith as a creative artist, that perhaps it would be better to stop writing for a year or two. I can no longer come up with anything new, my work is empty of content, I need a rest . . ."

The wife spreads more Bio-Placenta on her face and keeps mum.

"Am I right?" I ask, very tense. "Tell me the truth, am I right?"

The wife turns a quizzical glance on me. "Ephraim," she says quietly. "We've got to buy the kindergarten teacher something."

"When?"

"She's leaving at the end of the week, they moved her to Beersheba. We've got to buy her something on behalf of the mothers."

Her reply does not quite satisfy me from the purely factual point of view.

"Tell me," I throw at the little one, "why don't you listen when I'm talking to you?"

"I'm listening," the wife says and clogs up her pores with some brick-colored ointment. "I remember every single word you said."

"Well, what did I say?"

"Tell me, why don't you listen when I'm talking to you?"

"Right. So why don't you answer?"

"I'm thinking. That's why I don't answer."

True, my problem is not an easy one, I have to admit that.

"Do you think I ought to make an intellectual effort to overcome my momentary weakness?"

The little one does not answer.

"Are you listening?"

"Of course I'm listening, I'm not deaf. An intellectual effort to overcome that whatdoyoucallit at the moment."

"So?"

"A bonbonnière."

"What?"

"It's inexpensive, a bonbonnière, and yet impressive as a present, right?"

"Right," I agree without arguing, "but that does not solve my problem, darling. If I stop working for a year or two, what would fill the intellectual void created?"

The wife lets fly at her cheeks with a salvo of light slaps. Her eyes say "kindergarten teacher."

"Are you listening at all?"

"Don't ask me all the time whether I'm listening. The intellectual void created, what the hell!"

She really remembers every word.

"I think," I say, "that for a start I'll do a little painting and music.

"Why not?"

"Then I'll learn hippopotamus knitting."

"Quite." She passes a piece of blotting paper over the Bio-Placenta. Eyebrows raised. "In any case," she mumbles, "one has to think of all eventualities."

I have nothing to add on the subject, so I keep quiet.

"Ephraim," thus the wife, "why are you so quiet?"

"I'm not quiet, I'm only considering whether it isn't high time we exhumed the body of our servant girl and packed it into the green suitcase."

The little one is busy with the tweezers. She leafs absently through a foreign women's magazine.

"Aren't you listening?"

"Pack our servant girl's body in a suitcase."

Every word. She passes over her eyebrows with a

little foreign-made brush. Turns on the transistor. Light music.

"If President Nixon doesn't object," I let my thoughts spin on, "we'll buy the teacher a young zebra if we get it as a bargain."

Not even this works. There is no ignition.

"Sure." The little one massages her throat upward-downward. "Very good."

"In that case," I sum up the evening's discussion, "I'll hop over to my favorite concubine and spend the night with her. Are you listening?"

"I'll spend the night with her."

"So?"

"I still think a flower vase would be most suitable."

She rises and walks to the bathroom to wash off the brick. I'm left alone with my feverish thoughts. Seems I'll have to go on writing for a while. But what to buy the kindergarten teacher?

❧ Besides Bio-Placenta Cream, the beauty of Israeli women is also enhanced by the greatest invention of our century, contact lenses, which quickly turn a bespectacled housewife into a blind glamour girl.

In the Eye of the Storm

"Ephraim," the wife asked, "am I beautiful?"

"Yes," I replied, "why?"

Believe it or not, it seems that the little one had been mulling over this problem for quite a while. She knew only too well, she allowed, that there was nothing special in her, but still there was something in her, or rather there would be, she stressed, if it were not for those glasses . . .

"A bespectacled woman," she said, "is like a pressed and dried flower."

This, of course, was not an original thought. The little one had read it somewhere. In a newspaper ad pushing the most epochal invention since the wheel: contact lenses. They are the in thing now all over the world, two little glass lenses barely five millimeters in diameter which you simply place on your eyeball and voilà! Society doesn't suspect a thing, while your sparkling eyes see everything. It's absolutely marvelous, especially for short-sighted actresses, basketball players and spinsters. The lenses spread like wildfire all over our country. "A Haifa fashion model," her friends related, "started wearing her micro-lenses only a few months ago, and today she is already the divorced wife of a good-looking Latin American millionaire."

Everybody is recommending the miracle lenses; down with the old, obsolete, uncomfortable spectacles which put a glass partition between ourselves and beautiful female eyes.

"I've got the address of an expert," thus the little one. "Are you coming along?"

"I?"

"Isn't it for you that I want to be beautiful?"

We found about a thousand clients in the waiting room, most of them quite familiar with the use of microlenses. Some had got used to them to such an extent that they could not even tell for sure whether or not the lenses were in their eyes right now. That was probably the reason for their coming to the optician; what other reason could there have been? A middle-aged gentleman was just then demonstrating the ease with which he could place the glass sliver in his eye: First he put it on his fingertip, then, look, he moved it straight toward his eyeball and without batting an eyelid . . . Hey, where is the lens? It's dropped to the floor. Don't move! *Don't move!*

We took advantage of the uproar and slunk in to the specialist. He was a nice young optician, bursting with faith and enthusiasm, a genuine optimist. "It's all very simple," he explained, "the eye gradually gets used to the foreign body and after a while it all becomes a natural process . . ."

"Just a sec," I interrupted. "How soon?"

"That . . . depends . . ."

The expert carried out a number of psychosomatic

tests and declared that my wife's ocular climate was particularly suited to the wearing of micro-lenses. Also he
demonstrated how we place the glass with our finger in
the center of our eyeball and how we remove it six
hours later with a single flick of our wrist. The wife
gasped, but she was ready to suffer for the sake of
beauty. Exactly a week later she received her perfectly
ground micro-lenses, in a tasteful plastic case, against
payment of a mere IL300. That very evening at an intimate family reunion she started the gradual breaking-in
process, according to the rules: first day, fifteen minutes; second day, twenty minutes; third day . . .

Third day? What third day, if we may ask?

In other words, it's a question of guts. The wife
rinsed a lens, as she had been told, placed it on her
fingertip, then moved in on her eyeball as if she were
accusing it. *J'accuse!* And then what happened? The
finger kept growing, grew, grew, as in the movies, until
in the end it became absolutely huge and frightening.

"Ephraim," the wife faltered, "I'm afraid of my
finger!"

"Don't be silly," I encouraged the little one. "If for
nothing else, you must go on for the sake of the IL300."

The wife recovered her composure, squinted at the
approaching finger with death-defying determination
and—hup! As the finger reached the target area, her
glance swept sideways and the lens stuck with a squelch-
ing sound to the white of her eye. One has to admit, the
little one has never been a crack shot! It took the better
part of half an hour until the lens lazily rolled onto the
pupil. But then it was wonderful! No spectacles, and yet
the eye kept its natural beauty and sparkle, a real mar-

vel! Naturally, there were still certain side-effects; for example, the head muscles were temporarily paralyzed and the face was staring at the ceiling, this being the only way my wife could peek out without blinking from under her almost completely closed eyelids. Because the blinking somehow wouldn't come off. To tell the truth, even the slightest move of her toes caused my wife such excruciating pain as would have shamed the most expert torturer of the Holy Inquisition. The wife sat on a chair like a deep-frozen mackerel, motionless, while tears flowed from her eyes staring heavenward. Fifteen minutes later she removed the lenses in a panic.

Or, rather, she would have removed them. Those inanimate objects were having a field day on her pupils. The unfortunate woman frantically tried to remove them the way the young crook had shown her, but they simply wouldn't budge.

"Don't just sit there and stare at me," the little one shrilled like a trapped weasel. "Do something! *Do something!*"

I was terribly upset. After all, it was for me that the little one was suffering. I overturned a couple of drawers, looking for some instrument, but found only a pair of rusty pliers. And all the while she cried, the poor darling. "It hurts," she yelled, "it hurts!"

I called an ambulance. "Help," I roared. "Two micro-lenses have fallen into my wife's eyes. Please hurry!"

"Look, fella," thus the ambulance boys, "why don't you take her to an optician?"

I wrapped my wife across my shoulders, carried her down to the car and raced to the specialist. Before you could blink an eye, he had gently removed the glasses. "Not bad for a first try," he said. "Carry on." As a parting gift, he gave us a little rubber pump, somewhat like the contraption used for cleaning out clogged kitchen sinks, only much smaller, naturally. This little pump has to be affixed to the lens, straddling the pupil; a vacuum is thus created, and without difficulty the lens is removed.

Greatly encouraged, the wife continued her experiments with the micro. I would never have believed what punishment the human eye can take. Every morning at ten o'clock sharp the wife overcame her panic and inserted the lenses, then cautiously rose from her chair and slowly, painfully, tiptoed into my room. With her eyes brimming over, the poor mackerel stopped at my desk and wistfully asked me: "Now guess, are the lenses in or aren't they?"

This was in line with the ads which had said that it was quite impossible to detect the presence of the microlenses with the naked eye. That was the reason for their great popularity. Friends and acquaintances who visited my home during these historic days will certainly remember the appalling sight of my wife tottering through my study, her dry lips feverishly muttering: "I can't stand it any longer . . . I can't stand it . . ."

The poor darling had become very ugly. Her eyes were always red from extraordinary exertion, her face bloated with crying, and she looked quite shriveled. What suffering the woman went through! It was enough to break your heart! And the ordeal kept getting longer and longer! And the daily mad dashes to the optician to remove the glasses. The little pump was a complete flop. Only once did the wife succeed in using it: she carefully applied it to the lens, a vacuum was created, then—*glupp*—she almost extracted her whole eye (a near miss, these things happen sometimes). Nor will I ever forget that eerie Tuesday when my wife showed up in the doorway livid and trembling. "The left lens has slipped behind the eye and is now inside my skull!"

At this point I seriously considered hiring a permanent nurse for removal purposes. There was also some talk of emigrating as well as divorcing, in the pattern of the handsome Latin American millionaire. Small wonder if my anti-optician ideology became ever more extremist, though there is nothing one can do where female beauty is at stake. But just when I had lost all hope, literally at the last moment, I had a lucky break. The lenses got lost! How and where, we don't know to this day. They are so small, these lenses, that it is enough for somebody simply to tap the bottom of their box in front of an open window and the wonder lenses disappear in the city traffic. Possibly I had done the tapping myself.

The wife almost fainted. "What's going to happen now?" she yammered. "Now, when at long last I've become used to them . . ."

I took her tortured face between my two palms.

"Old girl," I said, "go back to spectacles!"

This, if you don't mind, is the final stage of miniaturization. The first day, fifteen minutes; the second day, twenty minutes; after two weeks—spectacles. Naturally, one does not have to give up entirely. From time to time one may show up at parties without spectacles, bragging to one's friends how marvelous those contact lenses are. Provided one can avoid crashing into the cupboard, the effect is electrifying. Everybody will swear that there is nothing in one's eyes, a real miracle. Deeply impressed, all my wife's friends have already gone to the specialist. Let them, it's the fashion now. My own little wife is completely cured of the fad and her beauty shines in its former perfection. It's fantastic.

❦ *"Don't put off until tomorrow what you can do today," the well-known enervating proverb says, and the Jewish people have adopted it without protest. Except where the payment of debts is concerned. Because in this sensitive field subconscious streams are working in an exactly opposite direction. Rumor has it that the Ten Commandments were actually eleven, the eleventh being: "Thou shalt not pay." But Aaron, Moses' brother, struck this off because, it will be remembered, he happened to be in charge of Internal Revenues.*

Fuhrman Pays

On Wednesday at 5:00 P.M. I went again to see Fuhrman. I had made up my mind: this would be the last battle. This time Fuhrman would pay, or else. About four months ago Fuhrman had commissioned a publicity slogan for his factory, and to this day I had not received my fee. At first I had hoped that he would pay without being asked, but as this did not come to pass, I inquired politely what was the matter? Fuhrman asked me to submit a bill. I submitted a bill for IL25 and waited, but nothing happened.

I went to Fuhrman and we agreed to meet at the end of the week and settle this little matter. We met at the end of the week. Fuhrman asked me what I wanted to discuss with him. I said: "I'd like to get my money." "Ah," said Fuhrman, "of course." He promised to phone me soon. Two months later I called again at his

place. He asked me what could he do for me? I said:
"IL25." "Oh," Fuhrman said, "of course, but right now
I've got terrible heartburn, please come at the end of
the week." I said to him: "Look, Mr. Fuhrman, it's a
matter of a measly twenty-five pounds." He asked me to
come back Friday morning. I came, but he was busy, so
I had to wait outside. When at last he came out, I was
furious.

"Tell me, Mr. Fuhrman," I accosted him, "how
much longer will I have to wait for my money?"

Fuhrman threw a mean, hostile glance at me:
"Come at five thirty on Wednesday."

So this was the Wednesday. I had arrived at five
for fear of being preceded by some heartburn. I let myself into Fuhrman's office and, without saying a word,
locked the door and pocketed the key. Fuhrman threw
a glum glance at me; it was obvious he had forgotten all
about me and had stayed in the office only by mistake.
Frowning, he looked at his watch, then tried an anemic
smile. Come to think of it, Fuhrman is not an evil man.
He only hates to pay. Nobody likes to pay, but he likes
it even less. His fortune is estimated between thirty and
forty millions—he owns a number of banks and forests.

"Take a seat." Fuhrman settled down in his armchair. "What can I do for you?"

I told him I had come for the twenty-five pounds.

"This morning I was at a funeral," thus Fuhrman. "We buried poor Shmulevitz. Such a crowd came
to the funeral. The old man was well liked. Did you
know him?"

"No."

"I still haven't recovered from the shock. I cried

like a little child. One can almost feel death's wings . . ."

I recognized the danger in the nick of time. Now he would say we are made of dust and return to dust, it's not worthwhile kicking up such a row for IL25, the Grim Reaper may gather us up any moment now.

"Life goes on, Mr. Fuhrman," I whispered. "We've got to carry on with the little trials and tribulations of everyday life."

"You're right. We've got to carry on." Fuhrman sighed and rose to leave the office. But the key was in my pocket, the door locked. I again mentioned the matter of my payment. Greatly puzzled, Fuhrman asked what payment I was talking about. I explained to him that he still owed me twenty-five pounds.

"Oh yes, now I remember," thus Fuhrman. "I'll write you out a check." I asked whether I couldn't have cash. He looked at me, shocked: IL25 in cash? Then he started examining his calendar to see on which day I could come and fetch my check.

"No, Fuhrman," I whispered hoarsely. "Now!"

"As you like, if you insist. Cup of tea?"

"Thanks," I said, "it's too hot for tea."

Fuhrman said he needed a drink. I opened the door and, holding on to his arm, walked him to the end of the passage. Fuhrman ordered half a cup of tea. Back in the office, he complained of the tea vendor's exorbitant prices. Fuhrman has about eight factories and mines. Two supermarkets. I locked the door again and pocketed the key.

The situation was quite clear. Fuhrman was marking time in the hope that time would be working for him. Any moment now something unexpected might happen. A war, nuclear attack, earthquake, you name it.

"There were times when we made four pennies in the orange groves," Fuhrman reminisced, "and lived like kings on that."

"Will you please make out a check?"

"As you like." Fuhrman rummaged around in his pocket. The checkbook was not there. Tomorrow maybe? I reminded him that the checkbook was obviously in the desk drawer. No, no, out of the question. Yet he opened the drawer. What do you know? At least ten books. The tea vendor knocked at the door. While I let him in, Fuhrman quickly locked the drawer. As I stirred the tea, the alarming thought flashed through his mind that he had left the heartburn pills at home.

"Never mind," I said, "I've got Alka-Seltzers on me."

Fuhrman blanched. Only now did he realize that I was in earnest, that I had come prepared. He sipped his tea with furrowed brows. Poor Shmulevitz, may he rest in peace, only last week he was still sitting in this very chair. My check, please. Oh yes. But he didn't have anything to write with. I handed him my ballpoint pen. The widow was absolutely heartbroken. Most people had liked the old man.

A slight shudder runs through Fuhrman's body. He opens his checkbook. "So it's twenty pounds?"

"Twenty-five."

Fuhrman becomes pensive, he nods sadly. My pen doesn't write. He is trying, but it just won't write. So there is nothing to be done but to go home and settle it another time. I have brought another pen. Unfortunately, this one does write. So it's twenty? Twenty-five. All right, twenty-five. I can see from his trembling earlobes that he is still thinking of the late Shmulevitz. I say to him: "Please hurry up, Mr. Fuhrman, I've got to go home sometime." The first beads of sweat appear on his forehead. Fuhrman's glance skips nervously across the room. The key is in my pocket. Fuhrman writes out my name and carefully dots the i. The phone rings. What relief! Conceivably, it's one of his men hired just for this purpose. Fuhrman chats for half an hour. It's late, he says in the end. He has to leave. His brother is sick. I lift the paper knife on his desk. Fuhrman watches me keenly. Heinrich has been bedridden for the last five days. The doctor thinks it's a virus. His brother is an artist, recently returned from Mexico.

"The check, Fuhrman!"

I can feel my eyes burning. Fuhrman realizes now that the smallest tactical error could cost him his life. He rises slowly to his feet and backs away from the desk. He has a sister as well, interior decoration. A family of artists. I follow him. He goes to concerts himself. Especially Tchaikovsky, Bartók. Fuhrman moves toward the window. I quickly cut him off. Still, Beethoven is Beethoven. The Ninth. He had planned to jump out of the window and then, with a broken leg, home by taxi, quickly pack a suitcase and out to the airport. Now he is forced back to his chair. "Sign it, Fuhrman, sign the check or else your last hour has come."

He signs.

In his eyes there is a great deal of human suffering. He does not hate me or loathe me, he only despises me because of my stinginess. I feel exhausted myself. I went through a great deal during the sad days preceding the Second World War, but I can't ever remember such tension.

Before my mind's eye there appears a chart illustrating the number of calories used up by the human body: woodcutting, 2,500 calories; breaking wild horses, 4,600 calories; check from Fuhrman, 9,700 calories.

Fuhrman leafs through the calendar. It is now June. July, August, September, October, November, December, January, February—here he stops, ponders. Then writes it down: February 28. I ask him to kindly write it out for an earlier date, say January. Sorry, but that's impossible, people are not paying him either, he has to make sure the check is covered. It is a hopeless argument. Fuhrman has aged considerably in the past few hours. His cheeks sag, there are rings around his eyes. He has turned completely gray. Yesterday the papers reported that he was taking over the state-owned steel mills.

All that is left now is to write down the year on the check. With that, the check should be complete. Goodness! Fuhrman is staring at the ceiling, his bloodless lips muttering a mute prayer. The earthquake is late. 1-9-7-Fuhrman wipes his brow. Drinks from the empty teacup. Then looks deeply into my eyes. A shiver runs down my spine. Now he hates me, maniacally, eternally and irrevocably. Fuhrman grips pen number two and hovers over the check.

"Wouldn't you like to go to the theatre?" he asks in a dying voice. "I've got a ticket, if you hurry you could still make it . . ."

The paper knife points at him. Silence. Poor Shmulevitz. Tchaikovsky. End of the line. The game is over. He inserts the missing "1" to make it 1971. Finished. The pen drops out of his lifeless fingers. His face turns into a death mask. His skin is yellow, his glance bemused. I take the check. His hand stretches out listlessly and drops like a mortally wounded dove. I take leave—" 'Bye, Mr. Fuhrman, thank you very much and sorry for the disturbance . . ."

Fuhrman does not answer, only stares at me with glassy eyes.

The earth no longer revolves. Time has stopped.

Fuhrman has paid.

✿ "Whom do you like better, your daddy or your mom?" Infantile relatives ask our joint son Amir, and the baby, if only he could talk, would answer unhesitatingly: "I don't favor either of them, I won't let either of them loaf around!"

Mummy, Daddy at Dead of Night

It is a well-known fact that I always avoid giving our family affairs a literary airing. After all, nobody gives a hoot what's going on in our home. Take, for instance, our baby boy Amir. The kid is amazingly well developed; in our doctor's opinion, his intellect is about thirty to thirty-five percent above that of the reader's offspring. Amir has blue eyes just like King David and, accordingly, is red-haired as well. As you will admit, this is fascinating stuff, yet I don't think it belongs in the public domain.

However, what happened one weekend not long ago can in no circumstances be passed over in silence.

Amir got up on his feet.

You don't believe it? True, sooner or later every kid gets up, but just imagine, Amir actually got up! It was a great surprise for all and sundry. At about 5:00 P.M. a totally unexpected victory yell came from the baby wing of our apartment, we dashed into the room and you could have knocked us down with a diaper: the child was holding onto the bars of his cot, standing on his own feet, unlike our country's economy. Our joy was boundless.

"Very nice!" we roared encouragement. "Very nice, Amir! Bravo! Once again!"

No, once again was out of the question. The child had learned amazingly early, or in any case not too late, the trick of getting up unaided, but it was not yet within his means to sit down again. And since such a little child cannot stand all day long on his feet, my darling beamed a May Day signal that we should sit him down again. The child likes to stand. He adores it. So about seventy times a day the call goes out from his quarters:

"Daddy! Daddy!"

It is to me he calls, to his daddy, who sired him. There is in his call something deeply moving. His mother revolves around him all day long and stuffs him with all sorts of mashes, while I, because of my extraordinarily tight schedule, hardly manage even to see him. But the child, with his marvelous, almost atavistic instinct, feels—knows—whom in the family he can trust implicitly. So whenever Amir gets up and cannot sit down again, he yells:

"Daddy! Daddy!"

And Daddy comes. In whatever position I may be, vertical or horizontal, when my child calls I drop everything and rush to his bedside. To be quite frank, this is a severe blow to the wife's prestige; even I feel embarrassed that her progeny should so clearly and unequivocally favor his father. Fortunately, my wife is an intelligent, enlightened female who manages to conceal her obvious jealousy. What's more, she even reassured me in so many words.

"It's quite all right, Ephraim," the wife said as I returned from one of the enthroning ceremonies, "don't mind me. He loves you, and I'll have to resign myself to that."

The only trouble is that one has to sleep from time to time, hasn't one?

As long as the kid got up and then couldn't sit down during the daylight hours, I went into action uncomplainingly. But when the game was moved to the wee hours, a certain nervousness could have been detected in me by a keen observer or a myopic imbecile. I need at least three hours of sleep a night, otherwise I stutter. But the brat wouldn't grant me even that. On that memorable St. Bartholomew night I rolled off my couch about thirty times to extend first aid whenever my son yelled:

"Daddy!"

The wife slumbered on peacefully and only from time to time did there appear around her lips a slight, forgiving smile as she listened to the eerie yells. I was not angry with her; after all, my son was calling me and not her. Yet there was something disturbing, one might even say maddening, in the fact that I, the overworked paterfamilias, should commute between my bed and the child's cot while a professional, unemployed mother quietly snored next to me! In all sincerity, I bore Amir a grudge. First of all, by now he should have learned to sit down by himself like the rest of the adolescent infants. Secondly, it was most unfair to behave like that toward his dear mummy, who cares for him all day and stuffs him with mashed potatoes. The kid is red-haired, as I said before.

"Amir," I therefore said to him one day while the wife was loafing at the hairdresser's, "don't always shout 'Daddy'! shout 'Mummy,' do you hear, my boy? Mummy, Mummy, Mummy, Mummy, Mummy, Mummy, Mummmmmmyyy!"

Amir is very bright, and the wife goes very often to the hairdresser's. I shall never forget the historic night when the first rebel yell floated in from the nursery:

"Mummy! Mummy!"

I stretched out my strong right arm and shook the wife awake.

"Mother," I whispered into the night, "your son is standing!"

The wife pricked up her ears. Then, as the May Day call sank in, she rolled off her couch. As she returned from the seating ritual, she threw me a trenchant glance, but did not say anything.

"Better be alert, darling," I whispered with feeling, "our son may well call you again."

And that is exactly what happened. During the coming weeks I enjoyed deep, refreshing slumber while the wife visibly withered on her mattress. Our blue-eyed wonder had found, under my guidance, the right way and after only a few lessons had completely grasped the importance of motherhood. The situation normalized. After all, a mother is a mother, what the heck! The wife got up whenever duty called her. If I remember rightly, she broke the record one night with forty sorties.

"I am really happy that the child returned to you," I said to the wife as she tried to pry open her glued-down eyelids. "It's so much more natural this way."

"Well, yes."

The idyllic situation ended as I was shaken up one dawn at five o'clock.

"Ephraim," the wife fluted, "he's calling you!"

And, indeed, the boy's voice could be heard pealing in the baby wing:

"Daddy! Daddy!"

So Amir has again switched over to me. A terrible suspicion is gnawing at me, though I dare not voice it. I seated my little boy in his cage and returned to my pallet, only to get up again two minutes later, while in the adjoining room the wife's eyes sparkled like so many bright stars. A mother's love overcomes everything. I am convinced that my sneaky wife is coaching our son for hours when I am not at home:

"Daddy, Daddy, Daddy, Dadddyyy . . ."

Small wonder that our ginger child cannot make up his mind at the present stage. Yet it is obvious that sooner or later he will have to take a decision on his seating policy. And then either his mother or I will have to go. To his cot, that is.

❦ *Let no one assume that we regret the color of Amir's hair. After all, one of the special characteristics of the Orient is a tendency toward gingerness in its inhabitants. Wherever you go, you meet flaming redheads, a real pleasure to behold. My little wife and I have always longed to have a red-haired child. But unfortunately we have three.*

Carrot-Head

In fact the term "red" does not quite do justice to the seriousness of the situation. Amir is practically purple, the kid is; his hair looks as if it were on fire. In his prime Chagall painted such combs on the elite among his roosters. Personally this does not bother me; on the contrary, there are a great many advantages to this phenomenon: if, for instance, Amir gets lost in a crowd, he can always be spotted by his color code. So what? So he won't be a bullfighter, big deal!

This should not be a conversational theme, really.

True, I must admit that, to the best of my knowledge, there was never a single redhead on my family tree; not even my great-great-grandfather had flaming hair. In any case, this is no catastrophe. History's greatest men were ginger-heads, a lot of people whose names I don't remember just now, and even Churchill, so the story goes, was born completely bald.

"In my eyes," the little woman says, "Amir is the most beautiful child in the whole world!"

To tell the truth, Amir shares this view. Even before he could walk, he would gaze raptly into the mirror and crow.

"I'm ginger," he would shout, "I'm ginger!"

He's really happy, the child. We, his worldly-wise parents, know only too well what lies in store for him. In kindergarten those cruel brats will start teasing him about the fire in his hair; little redhead, what's going to happen to you?

Our fears were realized only too soon. Hardly had eight months gone by when one day Amir came home from kindergarten bawling.

"A new boy," he mumbled, his eyes full of *Weltschmerz*, "he says . . . ginger . . ."

"He says that you are ginger!"

"No . . . that he is more ginger . . ."

It's a little difficult to understand him when he sobs. The teacher told us that a new kid had come to the kindergarten who was no less ginger-headed than Amir, and our sensitive son resented the loss of his monopoly. Luckily, in a matter of six minutes our son had forgotten the whole affair and went outside to be afraid of cats. But we, his parents, knew that he was sitting atop a roaring volcano.

"The child believes that to be ginger is very beautiful," the wife opined. "He's satisfied, happy. But what's going to happen next year, at the municipal kindergarten?"

The wife confessed that she often has nightmares in which Amirele is running down Allenby Road on his little legs and a cohort of kids (my wife always dreams up such rare words) is chasing him on a red fire engine, shouting: "Ginger! Ginger!" Frequently the woman's pillow is wet with tears the next morning. A mother's heart is like a sensitive seismograph; if she only eats something heavy for supper, the heart promptly reacts . . .

On that Wednesday, Amir came running back from municipal kindergarten!

"Daddy! Daddy!" the poor kid yelled. "They called me 'carrot-head, carrot-head'!"

"Did you fight them?"

"Why should I fight them?"

He does not realize, the boy, that they are trying to insult him. He thinks that carrot-head is a sort of vitamin-rich vegetable, and all day long he walks the streets, drunk with victory, shouting at the top of his lungs: "Carrot-head, carrot-head!"

My wife's eyes are filled with tears. For the time being, the child has no worries, he is free and gay, but we keep asking ourselves what will happen when he becomes wiser and one day, a day we dread, he realizes that to be ginger-haired means a life of unmitigated misery. He is so vulnerable and unprepared for this crisis.

"You are his father," my wife disclosed, "go and speak to him."

I lifted Amir onto my knees. "There is nothing wrong with being red-haired, son," I said to him with feeling. "No one is responsible for the color of his hair, right? King David's hair was a flaming red, and yet he beat Goliath. So don't let anyone tease you because you are ginger, my poor child. Tell them straight to their faces: 'Yes, I'm ginger, but my dad is not ginger!' "

Amir did not pay too much heed to my words, because he wanted to go out and toss rocks at the neighbor's puppies. He babbled something like "Never mind, Daddy, don't be sad because you aren't ginger"; the main thing was that he, Amir, was the nicest ginger in the whole kindergarten, a real carrot-head. That is, he persisted in his error. Redheads are awfully stubborn, there definitely is something irritating about them. It is not by chance that they are persecuted. Personally, I can understand it.

We did not press the point, but felt, the wife and I, that tension was building up. And when that vicious fight broke out in front of our house, we knew that the hour had struck. We dashed outside and found our son riding a bicycle and weeping like a gypsy violin, with older kids closing in on him from all sides.

I smashed through the ring of steel and hugged my darling. "Who called you ginger?" I roared. "Who calls my son ginger?"

The brats blinked, but dared not reply. They realized what a murderous mood I was in: anyone who so much as lifted a finger would do so at the risk of his life!

In the end Amir put things in their right perspective.

"What ginger, who ginger?" he asked. "I took Gilli's bicycle for a spin and he wants it back, but I ride it much better, so why does he always—"

"This is my bicycle," a thin kid stuttered, Gilli probably. "I didn't give it to him."

"You didn't, hey?" I lost my temper. "Because he's ginger, what?"

I carried Amir home in my strong arms. I washed his face with fatherly love.

"You are not ginger!" I said to him when the shock of the face-washing had worn off somewhat. "You are not at all ginger! Gingers have freckles on their noses, while you have just four and even those only in summer! A real ginger is a ginger all the way, not only in his ginger hair! Kings were gingers, the most beautiful animals in nature are ginger, like the fox and the hoopoe if its feathers happen to be ginger. But you are not at all ginger, Amirele, don't you believe it if they tell you that you are ginger, forget it, ginger . . ."

Do you think this helped? Once the kid gets hold of an idea, try to get him to let go of it! For a number of months now, he has believed that gingers are different. They feed them such nonsense in kindergarten. A few nights ago I caught Amir in front of the mirror, counting the freckles on his nose. My wife claims that he is secretly trimming his red hair. This is what we have been afraid of all along, and now here it is.

My wife was utterly dejected. "Why," she lamented and her eyes were red. "Why do they pick on him?"

There is no reasonable answer to this. Our hearts go out to ginger kids, especially to those whose parents don't help them get rid of their complexes. Not all of them are as lucky as our Amir.

❧ *Power corrupts, absolute power leads to absolute corruption. The Israeli baby is completely corrupted. It rules its household with no fear of competition and breaks down any opposition to its rule with steadfast crying.*

The Dangerous Cocoa Games

Amir the Red Menace doesn't eat well, never has eaten well. He simply doesn't like to chew on anything except pacifiers. That's how he was born. Experienced mothers advised us to starve him—not to feed him for several days until he came crawling on all fours. So we didn't feed him for several days and Amir became so weak that he crawled on all fours. We took him to an eminent professor, an expert in infant feeding, and the great man just threw a fleeting glance at our son and asked:

"Doesn't he eat?"

"No."

"He never will, either."

In other words, the professor drew on his immense experience and realized that there was absolutely nothing to be done here. This child has the absorptive capacity of a bird. We paid the professor an adequate fee, and since then we force-feed our Amir mornings and evenings, in the spirit of "By the sweat of thy brow

shalt thou eat bread." As a matter of fact, the little one
and I have no patience for such things, but fortunately
my wife's father has found in this his life's vocation: he
tells his grandson fantastic stories and Amir gapes and
forgets not to eat.

The main problem is, naturally, cocoa. This nutri-
tious drink is vital to Amir's physical development,
being chock-full of vitamins, minerals and lots of car-
bon dioxide. So Granddad locks himself in the nursery
with Amir for a whole evening and finally emerges exhausted and shaking, but with the joyous tidings:

"He's drunk half . . ."

The turning point came in midsummer. One hot
evening Granddad came out of the nursery hardly able
to speak with excitement.

"He drank the whole glass of cocoa!"

"You don't say," I gasped. "How did you manage
that?"

"I told him we're going to fix Daddy," the crafty
grandfather divulged. "Now we're going to fill up the
empty glass with tap water and we'll lie to you that
Amir hasn't drunk a drop, and you'll be terribly angry
and then we'll tell you that we've fixed you."

I found this quite a primitive trick, but under pressure from the wife ("the main thing is that the kid
should drink the cocoa") I cooperated. Granddad left
the bathroom holding the glass with the awful concoc-
tion in his hand and said: "Amir hasn't drunk a drop!"

"Boy, am I angry!" I shouted. "Boy, am I going to
smash things! So I'll drink the cocoa myself!"

The eyes of my son Amir sparkled like diamonds
when I tasted the mess.

"Phooey, what's this?"

"We fixed you! We fixed you!"

Amir did a wild, uninhibited jig and laughed like a tinkling bell, but the main thing was that he had drunk the cocoa, to quote my wife.

Next day, the same story. Granddad comes from the bathroom carrying the slops, boy am I angry, boy am I going to smash things, we fixed you, we fixed you. And since then, every night—the rites of cocoa, with the precision of a well-oiled Swiss parking meter. Since August it has worked even without Granddad (after all, the child is developing). Amir walks into the bathroom, boy am I angry, I fixed you, bell, diamonds . . .

By then I had begun to worry a little bit.

"Darling," I asked the wife, "is our child stupid?"

Because for quite a while the question had been puzzling me: What does our bright-eyed boy really think? That I keep forgetting every evening what's been going on weeks now? That I am that obtuse? The wife opined that it was immaterial what the kid thought, the main thing was that he drank the cocoa.

Indeed, it is hard to fathom a child's mind. Once— if I'm not mistaken, it was in the middle of October—I didn't taste the fluid before the "Phooey, what's this?" but poured it straight into the toilet.

"Phooey, daddy!" My son burst into tears. "You didn't taste it!"

The blood rushed to my head. Who does he take me for? "No need to taste it," I roared, "any fool can see it's only water!"

"Liar, then why did you taste it every evening until now?"

So Amir knew only too well that we were producing this idiotic show night after night. Then why did we have to repeat it all the time?

"It amuses him," the wife opined. "The main thing . . ."

Winter passed without a hitch. Early in November, Amir introduced a slight change into the dialogue, completing his reply as follows: "I didn't drink at all, this isn't cocoa, this is dishwater."

And late in December he started stirring the liquid with his index finger before handing it to me for expectoration. I hated the whole ceremony. In the early afternoon hours I began to shake at the very thought that at nightfall the little monster would show up with his sparkling eyes and laugh like a tinkling bell. Why can all the other kids drink cocoa without stage effects, and only I am stuck with such an infantile brat?

At the end of the Gregorian year, a shocking thing happened. I don't know what got into me, but on that evening I took the glass from my son's hands and, instead of spitting out the sewage in an arc, I drank it down to the last drop. It almost choked me, but I had to do it. Amir watched the performance spellbound, then switched over to high frequencies.

"Why?" my son shrilled. "Why?"

"What do you mean, why?" I replied with morbid glee. "Didn't you tell me that you hadn't drunk a drop, and that this wasn't cocoa, but dishwater? I said, OK, so I'll drink it myself, and I drank it, so what?"

Amir looked at me with burning hatred and wept all night. This proves that he knew all along that I knew it was water and that I was only faking. But if that were so, one may ask oneself: Who, damn it, needs this comedy every night?

The wife succinctly outlined her views. "The child," she said, "drinks cocoa and that's all that matters."

The cocoa rite continued unabated, night after night, as of 7:30 P.M. I didn't really mind it, no one is responsible for the deeds of his offspring, it's like an act of God, there's nothing one can do about it. Some parents are blessed with bright kids, others are less blessed —who can choose?

However!

On Amir's fifth birthday there was a slight change in showtime and we allowed our son to spend the evening in the company of his little pals. Amir locked himself up with them in his room and he took the brimming glass with him. A little later I prepared to walk in to speed things up somewhat, but I was brought up short in front of his door by Amir's voice:

"Now I've got to go to the bathroom to fill this up with water."

"Why?" Gilli asked.

"Daddy wants it that way."

"Why?"

"Dunno. Every night the same thing . . ."

So the child had believed all along that it was I who needed these games! He is observing the rites for my sake!

Next day I drew Amir to me. "Son," I said, "Daddy wants to stop this nonsense with the cocoa. It was nice, it was fun, but it's not educational. Come on, let's think of something else."

The little devil embarked on a solo which will be remembered for generations in the annals of our suburb.

The woman gave me a sound dressing down. "If the child stops drinking his cocoa," she announced, "he'll simply shrink down to zero."

So the show goes on. Sometimes my son shouts from the bathroom: "Daddy, may I bring the water now?" and I parrot the statutes: "Boy, am I angry, boy, am I going to smash things!" and utter despair grips me. One night when my son had the flu, I myself went to the bathroom, filled the glass with water and gulped it down.

"I fixed you!" My son's eyes sparkled like diamonds. "I fixed you!"

Lately he figured out a new variation in A minor: he walks out of the bathroom with the liquid and says my text by himself: "Boy, am I angry," etc. I feel slightly dizzy.

"What," I asked the woman, "doesn't he realize that *he* is talking and not I? So he thinks I'm talking when he talks? What's going on in this house?"

The woman's reply referred to the drinking of cocoa as a matter of principle. I think I'll have to see a doctor.

Israel is the only country in the world where the poor immigrants constitute a solid majority. This is why our arms are wide open for the reception of our brethren who keep coming all the time from the Diaspora. Question: How long can you hold your arms open?

The Russians are Coming

"Dear sir, let me be the first one to bring you the glad news on behalf of the Government and its institutions . . ."

"Mass immigration from Russia?"

"Yes! Within the framework of reuniting families, two hundred souls a month, as of Thursday afternoon."

"I'm fainting! May I embrace you, sir?"

"Bless you!"

"That's how I always was, sir! I signed all the petitions without looking twice. Let my people go!"

"Are you of Slavic origin, sir?"

"Only a sympathizer. What human material they are! Healthy, big, know how to enjoy their food, their drink, their fun!"

"They are simply wonderful!"

"How they dance, how they sing all day long! 'Otchi tchornyah!' And the main thing: every family has at least three or four kids!"

"Our future!"

"And they are industrious, sir, they are disciplined, thank God, they grew up under a Communist regime and are used to getting up in the morning and working hard! They are not like our Jews, they are a power! They'll be literally our salvation. I tell you, a great miracle has happened! This ought to change the map of the region, it will cure the economy, restore our morale! One cannot yet visualize the influence of this tremendous event on the course of world history."

"Thank you."

"You are welcome."

"Thank you again."

"Carry on! And best regards to the myriads of immigrants!"

"You may greet them personally."

"Unfortunately, my car is being repaired."

"No need to travel. They are coming here."

"Who is coming?"

"The Russians are coming."

"To whom?"

"To you, sir. Naturally, not all of them. Only one family."

"I have no family there."

"That doesn't matter. Every Israeli household has to play host in these days to one family from Russia. As a matter of fact, I came to notify you of this, sir."

"Is that the law?"

"For the time being, it's on a voluntary basis."

"So what do you mean, 'notify me'? Ask me!"

"I thought you were so glad, sir . . ."

"Of course I'm glad! You don't have to teach me! My house was always open to the mighty stream of Soviet Jewry! However . . ."

"Oh!"

"Dvora's music."

"I beg your pardon?"

"Let me explain. The only free place in our house is the guestroom, but that's where we placed the piano. My daughter is getting private lessons twice a week from Mrs. Pressburger, who's teaching at the Conservatoire as well. We waited two years before she agreed to take Dvora, and I can't simply throw up everything now."

"Couldn't the piano be moved elsewhere?"

"I thought of that myself. But where? The parlor is practically filled with the long cupboard. Ever tried to move a piano? It's no laughing matter."

"Only temporarily . . ."

"If you had only told me two weeks ago, before Dvora started taking piano lessons, maybe I could have done something for our Russian brothers, but now it's too late. Did you try the neighbors?"

"I did."

"Well?"

"Violin. Trumpet. Double bass."

"Well, that's how it is. As a matter of fact, did I get anything when I came here?"

"A three-room apartment."

"Only two and a half. But your Russians, if I'm not mistaken, are used to different living conditions. They grew up in abject poverty, believe me."

"So, nothing doing?"

"I didn't say that! I'm always ready to make sacrifices if that's necessary! Look, I'm paying taxes, ain't I?"

"And besides that?"

"Besides that, I need quiet in my home. Those people get up early in the morning and make a frightful racket, I know them, they sing and dance all day long, 'Otchi tchornyah, otchi tchornyah,' they drive you out of your mind. And besides, each of them has three or four children. They simply are not like the rest of us."

"So what shall we do?"

"That's indeed a problem. Do you pay something for taking them in?"

"No."

"Then I don't know."

"Should we send them back?"

"I'm afraid at this stage . . ."

"It's a pity, isn't it?"

"Only temporarily. In a few years' time, I hope, my daughter will complete her piano lessons, or Mrs. Pressburger will be pensioned off . . ."

🌷 *Knowledge of the Hebrew language is the key to full and happy citizenship in our country. It is therefore desirable that the new immigrant start speaking the country's language right from the beginning, even though his vocabulary may be restricted to the five basic expressions: "shalom," "thank you," "please," "why," "idiot." If he happens to learn a sixth, we are in trouble.*

A Plea for Selective Immigration

One afternoon recently I rang up Weinreb about a certain matter, never mind what. I rang his home, fully intending to give him a piece of my mind. Someone lifted the receiver.

"Hello," a scared female voice quaked, "hello."

"Hello," thus I, "who's speaking?"

"Don't know. Don't know no one."

"I'm asking who is speaking there."

"Here?"

"Yes, there."

"I'm speaking, hello."

"Who are you?"

"The new girl."

"Please call Mr. Weinreb."

"Weinreb? Where?"

"To the phone."

"Yes. Wait a moment."

"I'm waiting."

"Hello."

"Weinreb?"

"No. The new girl."

"I asked you to call Mr. Weinreb."

"Mister, you speaks Rumanian?"

"No! Please call Mr. Weinreb!"

"Yes. Hello . . . I can't now."

"What's the matter? Isn't he at home?"

"Don't know, hello."

"When is he coming back?"

"Who?"

"Weinreb! When is he coming home? Where is Weinreb?"

"Don't know," the new girl sobbed. "I just come of Rumania."

"Look here, my girl," thus I, with feeling, "I'd like to speak to Mr. Weinreb. He is not at home. All right. You don't know when he'll come back. All right. But surely you can tell him that I called, right?"

"Just a moment," the woman cried, "hello."

"What's the matter now?"

"I can't says, mister."

"Why not?"

"What's that Weinreb?"

"What do you mean, 'what's that'? Don't you know him?"

"You speaks Rumanian, mister? Just a little?"

"What apartment is that?"

"Kastelanetz Emmanuel. Hello."

"What number?"

"Seventy-three. Floor two."

"I mean what phone number?"

"Don't know."

"Isn't it written on the phone?"

"There is no phone here . . ."

❧ *Lately, to improve our balance of trade, we started exporting actors to the four corners of the world. They are in great demand, not only for their talent, but even more because they fill the theatres night after night with their Israeli visitors.*

Fiddler's Burden

In the center of London—or, to be more precise, in the center of the world—stands Her Majesty's Theatre, where they perform, as if this were the most natural thing in the world, the Jewish musical *Fiddler on the Roof*. The title role is played night after night by the famous actor Haym Topol with a large Israeli supporting cast. Topol has a contract with the theatre, but the Israeli cast changes every evening, depending on the flow of tourists.

The tie between them was forged way back in Israel, at the time that Mrs. Billitzer said to her husband in their first-floor flat in Tel Aviv. "And see you get tickets to *Fiddler on the Roof!*" Whereupon Billitzer got up and sent an urgent telegram to Mr. Topol, London, viz.: "TWO GOOD SEATS IN THE MIDDLE FOR JULY 22 BILLITZER."

Arriving in Britain, the Billitzers rush to the theatre and there find a monumental queue stretching for two blocks around the building and a sign in front of the box office to the effect that there are no tickets until October 11. Then why does this multitude nevertheless stand in line? They are lining up for Mr. Topol, to get to Mr. Topol through the back entrance. The elderly doorman makes superhuman efforts to stem the tidal wave and asks every Hebrew infiltrator whether Mr. Topol has invited him to his room.

"What do you mean 'invited'?" Billitzer fumes. "Do I need an invitation from him?"

And with that he crashes through to the illustrious actor with his wife Nehama and her sister, who also happens to be in London. That is, the Billitzer group actually needs three tickets in the middle, ha-ha-ha.

Topol's dressing room is divided into two wings, as behooves an international star. The actor himself is just then in the luxurious reception wing taking a long-distance call.

"You don't know me, hello," somebody at the other end of the line in Netania roars at him. "I've got a couple of English pals in London and promised them an invitation for next week, hello . . ."

"Next week? That will be difficult . . ."

"Why?"

Topol hasn't changed a bit, he has only grown a scraggly beard and his hair has become silvery at the sides. Also, a certain nervousness flickers in his eyes; this, it seems, is the price of success.

Avigdor from the Tel Aviv bus-terminal buffet is explaining things to him. "You are now succeeding here something extraordinary," Avigdor tells Topol. "You are now a famous actor, you've got to make hay while the sun shines. Don't sell yourself cheap, you can now get millions out of them, I'm telling you! I am quite ready to help you myself . . ."

"After the show, please," Topol pleads, "it's start-
ing soon . . ."

He tries to exchange a few words with Danny Kaye
sitting in a corner of the room, surveying the crowd
with a frightened glance. Just then the door flies open
and a group organized by a Tel Aviv travel bureau
bursts in. In their printed itinerary it says: "*Visit to
Hyde Park, Houses of Parliament and dressing room of
Haym Topol, intimate meeting with the artist, dinner
with him.*" The group's photographer is already immor-
talizing the event for the families. Second call—twenty
minutes to curtain time. Topol reads the cable which
has just arrived from the Middle East: "DOUBLE ROOM
WITH BATH FOR JULY 27 GREETINGS FRIEDMAN." His English valet returns from the street; he has bought on the
black market the additional ticket for Nehama Billitzer's sister. It so happens that Billitzer has no small
change, he'll send it in sometime tomorrow, good luck!
Topol dials the hotel for the room and bath, at the
same time, explaining to Mrs. Wexler, who clings to his
side: "Impossible, the theatre won't agree, madam. The
actors all have signed contracts . . ." Mrs. Wexler is
offering herself for the part of the matchmaker. She got
a lot of acting experience back in Poland, she'll learn
English, how much do they pay? Topol hands out autographs to a group of gaping London youths, and turns
down the invitation of a Jewish delegation from Bir-
mingham to become Chairman of their Community
and to sing and dance at their Christmas pantomime.
Yesterday they had tried to appoint him Bishop of
Liverpool, but he had refused, pleading he was too busy.
A blonde airline hostess embraces Topol: nine crew

members would like to come tomorrow, good seats if possible, money is no object because they haven't got a penny anyway.

Topol is already smearing black paint under his eyes so as to appear older, though there is no need for that, he looks old enough as it is. Avigdor, standing at his back, coaches him through the mirror: "A bit more make up at the side . . . no, there, there . . . enough!"

Third call. A new cable from Friedman: "TWO TICKETS TOURIST CLASS FOR JULY 27." A quiet-spoken gentleman dressed in black and wearing a top hat, with a wide red sash across his chest, the Lord Mayor of London, tries to reach the actor, but Topol says to him in Hebrew: "No more tickets, so help me, there aren't any left, call me tomorrow."

He is rather hoarse, Topol. "He doesn't take care of himself," Billitzer whispers to Nehama's sister, and pops a few menthol candies in the mouth of Tevye the Milkman. "What's your salary?" he asks him. "Is it true that it's ten thousand a night, is it?"

A little while later Topol's masculine voice floats in from the stage: "Tradition, tradition," and the folklore evening is on. The cool English public gets into a frenzy, applauds for minutes after each of Tevye's sentences and weeps like September rain when Topol says Chava is dead to him because she married a goy, tradition!

"Topol is my good friend," dozens of Israelis explain to their seat neighbors as the show goes on, "we are both from Israel . . ."

Eight curtain calls with bravos and stormy applause. When Topol takes his bow by himself, the

cheering threatens to bring down the roof, though it is
a little disturbing that he takes his last call with Avigdor and Mrs. Wexler on either side of him.

Masses of other Israelis are waiting for Topol behind the scenes. The excitement is understandable. "I
cried," Billitzer confesses, "I cried like a little child.
How the English public was moved! Good Lord, that
we lived to see this! But just between you, me and the
doorpost, Rex Harrison would have been better."

Other deeply moved spectators point out that,
after all, the majority of the audience were Jews and
that somehow makes Topol's success less glorious. "He
is good, no doubt about it, he is quite good," Avigdor
remarks. He himself sticks firmly to Topol and on the
way to the dressing room proposes to him a new joint
venture: one ought to print maps of London with the
names of the streets and sell them to the tourists. He—
Avigdor—would give his name and Topol the money.

"Nonsense," opines Billitzer, sticking to Topol's
other side, "only movies! He's got to go into movies now. My brother-in-law knows a Brazilian pro-
ducer . . ."

The British TV crew with their bulky equipment
are greatly hampering the work of the Israeli team.
They would like to shoot the "King of London Musi-
cals," as the critics have hailed him, but for technical
reasons are unable to approach the star. "I knew
Topol's daddy when you, sir, did not even know Topol
existed," Mrs. Wexler upbraids the TV cameraman for
his pushiness, "so don't tell me where to stand, will
you?" Topol in the meantime reads the latest cable:
"PROVIDE BABYSITTER FOR JULY 27 STOP SEND CASH FRIED-

MAN." Topol orders one of his secretaries to transfer £30 to Tel Aviv and closets himself with Danny Kaye in his private bathroom. The Israelis are offended by the humiliating discrimination, some of them so insulted as to leave the room ostentatiously and return fifteen minutes later bearing flowers.

"He's great, isn't he?" Billitzer asks someone in front of the door. "But his accent . . ."

"I beg your pardon," the addressed person replies. He is the Duke of Kent, who has come with his Duchess to congratulate the actor. Billitzer introduces himself and asks whether it would be possible to arrange an audience or something with the Queen. Life goes on in the meantime. A phone call from the Embassy: a delegation of fourteen members of the Knesset is arriving on August 8, kindly make the necessary arrangements— that is, in the middle. Avigdor puts the partnership on a new basis: 45 percent for him and 55 percent for Topol, but first the investment has to be recouped. Photographers set off their flashes as Topol comes out of the bathroom in a robe and spectators besiege him for autographs. Topol tries to smile. The Lord Mayor of London makes a date for Thursday with Mrs. Wexler and leaves, disappointed. The Duke of Kent gropes for his glasses on the floor.

The group gets ready for dinner with Topol. It has become well known all over the British Commonwealth that after every performance of *Fiddler* one eats at Topol's expense at one of the better restaurants in town. It is a sort of beautiful Jewish tradition. Even the taxi drivers know it: they park in front of the stage door shouting, "Topol Tours! Topol Tours!"

The Israeli group gets into nine taxis and orders, "Follow him!"

The convoy moves off toward the district where all the expensive restaurants are located. Topol, at the head of the armored column, takes out his wallet and checks whether he has enough cash on him to pay for thirty-six persons, including four London passers-by who have infiltrated the group. Topol looks a little tired, God knows why.

"Success has gone to his head," Billitzer remarks in the taxi to Nehama and her sister. "He is no longer the same sincere, nice Topol, it's a different man altogether, I am sorry to say . . ."

❦ Since we are in London, let's hop across the Atlantic to that hotbed of Israeli imperialism, New York. We Israelis have much in common with that city, though it cannot be denied that Jews have more influence there.

New York Ain't America

If anywhere in this shrunken world there exists a state within a state within a state, it is the City of New York, within New York State, within our sister-state overseas. New York has more people, more accidents, more exhibitions, more investments, more indecent acts than any other city in the world. What's more, New York is the residence of the U.N., Barbra Streisand and the King of Saudi Arabia. New York scrapes the skies. It is wide open twenty-four hours a day. There is only one New York, praise the Lord.

The sons of the United States are mighty proud of their New York. As soon as the little tourist leaves the megalopolis and starts his trek across the continent, folks keep asking: "How do you like America? On the other hand, what do you think of New York?"

"America is very nice," I answer, "and New York is cute."

With that I would have exhausted the subject as well as ruined my career in the U.S. but for the turn of events in Washington, D.C. In that beautiful but relatively small city I was sitting in an air-conditioned restaurant and in the company of a hospitable local luminary. He asked the inevitable question about America and New York.

"New York is cute," I answered, "though a little noisy for my money."

"Wait a second," the luminary said. "I've got to tell this to my wife."

With that he went to the telephone and reported: "He can't stand New York, the noise drives him crazy." Then he turned to me, receiver still in hand. "Jeanette asks what do you think of the dirt there?"

"It's nauseating."

"And the shots in the night?"

"Don't even remind me of them."

"My wife," said Harry, "invites you to dinner."

That's when I came of age. I got completely wise that night at Harry's in the presence of dozens of distinguished guests. The burghers of relatively small Washington crowded around me, cocktail glasses in hand, their eyes reflecting deep-seated inferiority complexes as well as mute prayers.

"Tell us," their tortured glances said, "tell us bad things about New York! You are a tourist, it's okay for you . . ."

"A nervous city," I obliged. "I could not live there even two years."

"Oh!" the Washington ladies sighed sensually. "More!"

"New Yorkers are short, money-mad and unshaven. New York ain't America."

"O Lord," a young reporter screamed. "That's my headline!"

With that he hurried to the telephone. Next day

the newspapers of the capital ran my picture under the headline: "ISRAELI SCIENTIST REJECTS HYSTERICAL NEW YORK," and a sub-heading: "*Admires Washington's Exquisite Beauty.*"

Small wonder then that in Texas I was mobbed by complex-ridden cowboys. At the Houston airport the head of the delegation stepped up to me, all seven feet of him, and said: "Hi! You the guy who cusses New York?"

"That depends," I answered. "What are the opportunities here?"

They gave me a suite at the Hilton, a car complete with chauffeur and an unlimited supply of ice. The formal dinner in my honor was attended by all the oil magnates in the neighborhood. They hardly touched their steaks, but just looked at me mutely, expectantly; when would I start talking at long last? The tension was unbearable. I sensed the heavy responsibility placed upon me.

"I'm sorry if this will offend you," opened the proceedings, "but New York is not all it should be. It is not a city, but a sleazy hashish den which ought to be closed down by police order!"

Such stormy applause had not been heard for years in southern Texas. After my short TV interview ("The height of the average New York giant is about three and a half inches less than that of a Texas midget") the invitations started rolling in from all over the States.

It was Charlie who saved my tour from complete anarchy. "You are hot stuff now," Charlie said. "Your New York gimmick is keeping them on the edge of their seats. What you need is an agent."

We signed a seasonal contract and Charlie printed my price list in an eye-catching layout: "*General remarks on overcrowded New York—invitation to a lavish dinner. Factual description of the breakdown in morals—two days' full board. Choice examples of monstrosity (with slides)—a week's hospitality. De-luxe general slaughter—the same with permission to invite friends. Cut rates for organized groups. Matinee on Wednesdays. Registration is now open.*"

In Los Angeles they rented me the Municipal Baseball Park where Billy Graham does his preaching. "Our keen-eyed friend here has just escaped from New York," the Deputy Mayor introduced me amid stormy applause. "Let's hear what he has to say!"

I grabbed the microphone. "Gentlemen, inhabitants of the West Coast, the beauty of your city cannot erase from my heart the suffering I underwent in New York. But I no longer feel any anger toward that modern Sodom, only pity, because it is nothing more than a sprawling slum, an asphalt jungle surrounded by stinking swamps in which ferocious alligators prowl, ready to tear apart the unwary for the sake of a dubious career of corruption and violence . . ."

That's how I turned poet. After my variation in A Minor on the theme of the Mafia which runs the unfortunate metropolis, I was carried shoulder-high by the Los Angeles elite until they got tired and fled to New York to have some fun. But by then I was moving under my own steam. A San Francisco record company proposed issuing an album with excerpts from my speeches, under the title: "I came to Bury New York, Not to Praise Her." But Charlie thought I should not overexpose myself at this stage, otherwise any American could purchase a long-playing curse on New York for $2.99 and achieve orgasm at home. "Let them pay for their entertainment," my agent said.

By then I was quoting from Dante's *Inferno* with organ accompaniment, and foaming at the mouth— Technicolor foam. Chicago went literally berserk when I described in a few words how the earth was going to swallow the sinful city one of these days.

"You hit the nail right on the head," they said in the Windy City. "May the Lord strike down those gangsters . . ."

A fanatic religious sect who called themselves "The Yorks" was getting organized. The United Jewish Appeal also showed interest in my series on New York. But my personal tragedy was that, as a matter of fact, New York is a rather interesting city, full of life and fun, unlike all those bum places where life ends every day at 5:00 P.M. There are a few monsters in New York? Where aren't there, if I may ask? You can't expect a city of twelve million or so to be made up entirely of saints. So they have a number of murderers, lawyers and witches. As a matter of fact, I like lively, colorful New York. I love its wonderful shortcomings. It's better to be a big-time pimp in New York than the owner of a small laundry in Buffalo. One thousand dollars is better than $350. We also live in Tel Aviv, don't we?

The truth burst out of me with irresistible force. "New York is the center of the world," I shouted at the top of my lungs into the sunshine. "New York is marvelous! New York ain't America!"

"Wait a second," someone said, "I've got to tell

this to my wife."

Actually, in the meantime I had come back to New York.

"A Broadway musical," I said, "is worth more than sixty thousand head of cattle in Arizona!"

"Our wives," said the New Yorkers, "would like to invite you to dinner . . ."

❧ From the Sinful City let's dash back to a staid and petit-bourgeois place like Hamburg, where the prosperous burghers every year turn in at a progressively earlier hour. Only two years ago lights-out in Hamburg homes was still 9:30 P.M. Today it is 7:45, and if the trend continues, in 1984 the city's inhabitants will go to sleep at 5:15 in the afternoon. Eventually they won't get up at all.

For Guests Only

The stranger who nowadays finds himself on the streets of Hamburg after nine in the evening gets the eerie feeling of walking in a ghost city, the deserted streets lending an air of a city after a nuclear attack. Here and there he may bump into a few reeling sailors, a halo of pure alcohol surrounding them, who conceivably may negotiate with him for a one-time tippling loan; apart from them, however, there is no sign of organic life on the streets of the metropolis.

Except for St. Pauli, the fun district at the edge of the city, where the music never stops before daybreak.

This pleasant enclave is a nice combination of Las Vegas and ancient Sodom. You find there garish gambling casinos, striptease joints geared for sexual enlightenment and mass shows guaranteed to bring blushes to the jaundiced cheeks of Singapore eunuchs, who come here for advanced training in the newest sexual-pathological methods. There are modern drug dens and card clubs for transvestites, to say nothing of the conducted orgies for the crews of ships berthing in Fun City. The only thing you don't find in St. Pauli is secrecy, the by-laws of the city of Hamburg being rigorously permissive toward the dozens of brothels, unique in Europe in that they beckon with blinking fluorescent lights to the weary traveler.

The honest citizens of Hamburg scorn St. Pauli and try to ignore it, though there is in their attitude a modicum of fatherly tolerance and their every move is a sincere apology for having to put up with this shameful blight in their midst because they are a port city and that just can't be helped.

Take our hotel manager, who told us a few evenings ago: "Personally, I wouldn't go to the District for all the gold in the world, but you, sir, as a foreign journalist, if I am not mistaken, you must see everything. However," the man added, "don't, under any circumstances, go there on your own, because those underworld types will drag you into one of the strip joints there and rob you of your last pfennig."

"Thank you so much," I answered, "but where in Hamburg could I find somebody ready to accompany me there?"

"That indeed is a problem, because your escort would have to be a man of the world like myself," the hotelier mused and turned to his wife. "What do you think, dear?"

"I think," Gertrude said, "that you yourself ought to accompany the gentleman."

The hotel man winced. "No, anything but that, darling!"

"Sometimes," thus Gertrude, "one has to make

sacrifices for one's guests . . ."

And then the man and his wife got into a big argument until in the end my hotel manager broke down and promised to consult his agenda to see whether he could squeeze in a brief visit to a few sex-spots. And after only three minutes he came to me in the lobby with the joyful tidings.

"I have found the time for it."

"When?"

"Now."

He was already dressed for the kill and kept stomping on the spot impatiently, but I had not yet quite made up my mind because, personally, I graduated in the humanities in my youth and therefore am a little scared of male lesbians and things of that sort. So I said to my benefactor that I would think it over.

"All right," the man answered. "So tomorrow? Day after tomorrow? When?"

Luckily I was called to the telephone. A male voice introduced himself at the other end of the line as an active Israeli who had temporarily come to Hamburg with his family a few years ago and in the meantime had acquired a number of department stores, but definitely intended to go home very soon, possibly this year and certainly not later than the beginning of the next century, and in any case he was rooting for us, see?

"You certainly would like to see the city," the nice emigrant said. "Listen to the voice of experience: don't go to St. Pauli alone! Only yesterday I said to Tzippora: I won't ever let any of our friends fall into their clutches! I am busy up to my ears, but if you insist . . ."

"Thank you," I said. "I'll manage somehow."

"No, no, no," thus the emigrant, "those shameless women will chase you down the main streets in their undies, screaming horribly. I couldn't possibly let you go alone. Are you free tonight?"

We agreed to ring each other once every fifteen minutes. The hotel manager stayed glued to the telephone exchange, very upset about the leak, and kept signaling that I shouldn't trust anybody but him. Just then there was a call from the desk: the radio people had come and were preparing a very original sort of interview: I would be walking somewhere in the city, it didn't really matter where, let's say in St. Pauli, and they would trail me with their roving microphone, recording everything that went on inside those filthy houses. I found the proposal rather interesting, but then the hotel porter drew me aside and told me confidentially that those jerks were just looking for a pretext to visit the whores, while he was coming off his shift at 11:00 P.M., exactly when in St. Pauli the monsters on duty put on their most thrilling atrocities.

"Don't go there without a trustworthy escort," the elderly porter warned. "They'll drag you into too expensive orgies. I'll just ring home and tell the family that a foreign journalist needs my help and then I don't mind if we go there for half an hour or so . . ."

The emigrant's cable arrived just then with a message that, if pressed, he was ready to move right away, while the hotel man hid in my room, his eyes mutely imploring me to ask him to come along. One could definitely feel a certain ferment in the city. The newspaper offices were swamping me with invitations to write something new, something risqué in the form of a lively report from the red-light district, if I am not mistaken, with myself flitting in and out of dark places and the paper's photographer following me and taking pictures. The editor himself might come along. And the sports writer. And the editor of the literary supplement and his assistants and his stable of writers and the owner of the printing shop and his stepfather.

"Of course you could also go by yourself," the chief editor said, "but I doubt whether you would get out alive. Only last week a couple of fags dragged a tourist into a doorway and forced him to tango with them. So better think twice . . ."

To tell the truth, by then I was somewhat alarmed, especially since as a rule I lost all interest in the fair sex for at least a month whenever I see one of those coeducational stripteases, and according to the vivid descriptions of my entourage, what went on there bordered on the surrealistic.

I therefore proposed to the crowd milling in front of the hotel: "How about going to St. Pauli without me?"

"That's ridiculous," the group's spokesman answered. "We are respectable citizens, we don't give a damn about that nonsense. We are simply worried that an important guest like yourself might get a wrong impression of our city."

The emigrant signaled to me from his luxurious car that he was ready to start any time. I realized that I would have to go through with this thing, otherwise Hamburg would be completely paralyzed.

"OK," I said, "Thursday."

The crowd began cheering and the good news

spread like wildfire through the city. A state of high alert was declared. The teleprinters clacked the code phrase: *"The timid voyeur will peek tomorrow,"* and someone told me that stringent traffic restrictions for next Thursday had been announced on the nine-o'clock news.

"Don't worry," the hotel manager tried to encourage me, shaking in his every limb, "we'll watch over you there."

The convoy was made up of about a dozen vehicles, among them a few buses packed with hospitable natives. At dead of night we parked at the edge of the notorious district and my escorts poured out of their cars, blinking perplexedly at the glaring lights. It seems that this was their first visit ever and they had no idea what to do. I guided them through the winding alleyways, pimps swarming around us like a school of fish. But they did not dare to drag me into any den, since I was not alone. The hotel manager clapped his hands like a little child at the sight of every single broad he met and his eyes filled with tears of joy while my entourage gradually dispersed, each according to his deviation. Therefore, when later on we returned to our fleet of cars, we found that some of our men had dropped out, among them a music critic and his cousin who had signed on with a local cabaret to perform indecent acts on the high trapeze. The hotel owner had also decided to settle down there temporarily as a confetti tosser at unspeakable orgies. I went back to sleep in the moral and orderly mother town, and dreamed that I was a hamburger being served in a hot roll to a well-known gynecologist of Prussian origin.

"Lo, the People Shall Dwell Alone"

That's how the Bible's reporter headed his exclusive interview with Balaam, and, quite frankly, to this day we don't know for sure whether he meant to praise or to curse us. Be that as it may, ever since, and to this day, we have maintained our special status as the only people in the world without a single ally. Our older citizens—that is, the Palmach fighters—probably still remember the newspaper ad we placed briefly after the establishment of the State:

> Small, isolated and orderly nation
> S E E K S
> wealthy partner to ensure survival.
> Written offers to "ForMin,"
> JERUSALEM.

We are still waiting for a response.

Our ears are tuned to the slightest rustle on this wave length, but for some reason no nation wants an alliance with us, not even the United States. A number of years back an American President declared in a moment of weakness: "Israel is of close interest to us"—

that is, he specifically said "close," which is the exact opposite of "remote," and the State Department promptly added that "the President was trying to express his desire to maintain good relations with all the states in the area." Most comforting. To say nothing of our country's traditional friend, the President of Upper Bingo, who declared during his stay here: "Our countries are linked together by b." That's how far the President got in his airport address before he was ousted by his brother-in-law. Only one statesman had the guts to say openly, "Israel is our ally," the ex-President of France, and he earned our deep respect for that. True, technically the idea has not yet been completely implemented, there are still certain difficulties, yet it is nice to remember that somebody once called us "ally" publicly—for the first and last time in history.

All these thoughts occur to the man-in-the-street as he walks along the Canal bank. On the other side of his secure and agreed-upon border the Egyptian batteries are standing cheek by jowl, peppering the dunes like a summer hailstorm, while on our side a young officer sits in his dugout with a sheet of paper in front of him.

"Cease fire!" he orders. "We have already fired twenty-two shells today, that's beyond our quota."

It's small consolation that we call all our shots while the hundred million wallowing in oil get everything free of charge. They have allies: Russia, China, France, India, everybody. We haven't got anyone, except Holzer.

We met Holzer somewhere in the Diaspora, at our Gentile hotel. He rang us up from downstairs, fairly early in the morning. The porter told him we were still asleep, whereupon Holzer told the porter it was all right to wake us up. "Simply tell him 'Holzer's here.'" So the porter woke us up and we asked him: "Who is Holzer?"

"I thought you knew him, sir," the alien porter stuttered. "I'll ask him right away . . . Where is he?"

By then he was in our room. A Jew with a nose which went out of fashion twenty years ago, small and squirming, with a bowler hat—Holzer.

"I'm from the Community," he introduced himself. "We heard you were an Israeli writer. Welcome, have you had your dinner, I know a Greek restaurant, I've got a clothes shop, came from Poland after the war, Michael Holzer from Haifa, Transports, is my cousin, been three times in Israel, wonderful, the Negev, now don't you withdraw, all the anti-Semites should drop dead, we donate every year, our Rabbi sends these flowers, why don't you dress, there's firing at Suez, isn't there?"

"I suppose so," we yawned. "Nice to met you, Mr. Holzer."

"Call me Al. And now you've got to come to the synagogue, they're all waiting for you."

"Dear Mr. Holzer," we said, pulling on our socks, "I'm most grateful for your invitation, but, with all due respect, I'm not observant."

"That's all right. You're an Israeli, a writer. You're a Jew. You've got to come."

"Last time I was in a synagogue was at my bar mitzva."

"Never mind. You don't have to do a thing. Not

even pray. Just sit there."

"If they call me to the Torah, I won't know what to do, Mr. Holzer."

"Call me Al. I'll fix it so the Rabbi won't call you. As long as you're there. Ten minutes. Just leaf through the prayer book. You've got to come."

"Why?"

"So they should see you."

Predictably, we let Holzer drag us to the synagogue, our head covered with a borrowed skullcap, our heart a-flutter with mute fear. Holzer walked before us like the proverbial pillar of fire before the camp. He went straight up to the Rabbi, deeply immersed in his morning prayer, and the Rabbi winked at us and waved in a friendly way, as if saying: "Don't be afraid, I won't call you to the Torah for all the gold in the world." The cantor raised his voice and intoned a personal blessing for the State of Israel, while the dozen or so Jews in their worn pews stopped rocking for a while and threw us amiable looks as if we and they were old, old acquaintances.

And we felt as if we and they were indeed old, old acquaintances.

Holzer sailed among the pews humming psalms, whispering to the notables, pointing at us, and in the end coming up and—grinning bashfully—enveloping us in a prayer shawl.

We looked at Holzer with his unfashionable nose, commuting ceaselessly between the Rabbi and the heads of the Community. He had short, bandy legs, the way the nice Gentiles drew him in gentler times, and his hat slipped back on his head as if he were talking to a client in his clothes shop. From time to time he blared "Yasharkoah!" at the top of his voice, dashed over to us and read in our stead from the prayer book, raising apologetic eyes heavenward, then engaged his neighbors in purely commercial conversation.

A little Jew by any standard, nothing special, Holzer.

For the past twenty years, ever since coming to Israel, this writer has made superhuman efforts to become swallowed up in the Great Semitic Space, to see in his neighbors his distant relatives, to fraternize with the notables of East Jerusalem, liberally sprinkling his conversation with Arab expressions. Sometimes, especially when partaking of Channel 5 by courtesy of the Hashemite Kingdom, it seemed to us that we were indeed on our way to becoming one of them, in love with shishkebab and baked lamb. But, kidnapped to that synagogue in the distant Diaspora, the realization grew upon us, as clearly as the sun at noon, that it was quite hopeless: we felt no attraction whatsoever toward the notables from East Jerusalem or toward the merchants of Nablus. We loved Holzer and that was that.

Because he loves us, because he loves Israel. Because Holzer's eyes shine with tears of joy whenever his fingers touch a phony emissary of the Jewish State. Because he is plagued by pangs of conscience twenty-four hours a day for not going to Israel, hires a Hebrew teacher from Jerusalem for his sons—and his sons don't learn a damn thing. Because these Holzers hand over their loot to the Keren Kayemet as naturally as if they were silent partners. Because they eat avocado, though they can't stand the sight of it. Because they blissfully sign their names in Hebrew characters more befitting a first-grade tot. Because we cannot do a foolish thing in an international arena that Holzer would not defend to his last breath. Because in his house there hang pictures of Moshe Dayan, Premier Golda and Jerusalem. Because when the Six-Day War broke out, this Community took a unanimous decision: as of that day, the whole property of the Community belonged to the State of Israel. Because they are so naïve, silly, observant, Zionist . . .

Therefore, at a time when half the world is preparing for the confrontation with us, and the East is saturating our neighbors with guns while we are getting a surfeit of advice from the West, we know all the same that somewhere in the world we have an ally, faithful and unflinching, certainly not less so than the Camp of Peace on the side of our neighbors—Holzer the clothier.

It's time we called him Al, really.

The avant-garde has taken over the Israeli theatre. Spectators who only five years ago did not understand a bloody thing about the modern play and roundly cursed that nonsense have now completely changed their outlook, and are full of praise for the new avant-garde plays, though they don't understand a bloody thing that's going on upstage.

Tribute to a Recumbent Giant

Saturday noon, crossing Frishman Street, I spotted Yarden Podmenitzki in the café, holding a whole table all to himself. He did not invite me to sit down and have a cold drink, and I knew at once what was the cause of his unusual reserve: last week the veteran actor had received rave reviews in the daily press for his acting in *Specks*. His part in that play with universal overtones was that of an aging procurer of male prostitutes, and he succeeded in riveting the audience to their seats with his natural and uninhibited acting. No less a personage than I. L. Kunstetter himself wrote that "the surprise of this remarkable evening is without doubt Podmenitzki, who literally exuded diabolic intuition. His Alphonso is a masterpiece of theatrical animality; each snort, every movement of his disjointed limbs, and first and foremost his inimitable silences, give him the undisputed status of a character actor *par excellence*."

"How right Kunstetter is, maestro," I said as I sat down at his table. "Your silence under the heavy baroque table in the third act sent shivers down my spine."

"That's what people keep telling me," Podmenitzki readily agreed. "Grinstein wrote after the premiere that my lying there under the table raised in him associations of conspiratorial nihilism or something."

"How fitting," I said. "There are lots of hidden symbols there. You come out of the theatre and for a number of days you can't stop asking yourself: as a matter of fact, why did Alfonso sprawl for a whole hour on the floor?"

"An hour and eight minutes!"

"Yes. What in fact is the director trying to say, if I may ask?"

"Of course you may ask. It's no secret. I asked him myself."

"And what did he answer?"

"That it is written into the play. So I answered him through one of the girls who understands French: 'Excuse me, Boulanger, it says in the text that I have to crawl under the table, but nowhere does it say that I've got to stay there until the end of the show.' So then he threw a fit in French, that if he wanted me to stay there for two months, I'd damned well have to stay there two months. I went straight to the management and told them that with thirty-eight years of rich dramatic experience to my credit, I wouldn't let that idiot keep me on the dirty planks and get splinters in my hands. They asked me especially to do Boulanger this favor, they were not going to rehire him anyway. At the time they didn't know he would get such exceptional reviews."

"That's right, they wrote that his direction was the puppeteering expression of our generation."

"That's obvious."

"All of them praise in particular the scene where you and the five male prostitutes straddle the sewing machine and cover your heads, each of you with a different-colored handkerchief. As a matter of fact, what does this mean?"

"A handkerchief is a little rag you carry in your pocket, and if, God forbid, you catch cold . . ."

"I know the meaning of the word 'handkerchief,' Mr. Podmenitzki. What I'd like to know is, what are you trying to say up there on the sewing machine?"

"Didn't you hear Avigdor Ben-Parrot at the Milo Club? Wait, let me see, I wrote it down somewhere. Yes, he says that 'the orgy of handkerchiefs is a kaleidoscope of perfectly paradoxal consciousness.' "

"That's clear, but what I'd like to know is, why do you cover your eyes?"

"Why! Why! Who can argue all the time with that Boulanger crackpot? He wants handkerchiefs—all right, let it be handkerchiefs! All I asked was that Mundek should launder my handkerchief every night, so do you think he does? Those rags have a musty smell. At the premiere Honigman whispered in the middle of the scene: 'Boys, I must sneeze!' All of us heard it, we were shaking with laughter."

"Honigman—isn't that the guy of whom they wrote that he was a virtuoso of the underplaying school?"

"Yes, he is quite a guy, he didn't sneeze until the intermission. He was afraid of Boulanger."

"But doesn't he ever explain anything to you?"

"Honigman? Why should he—"

"No, Boulanger!"

"Oh, him. To tell you the truth, he never stops. explaining, but personally I don't listen too carefully, because what he says is all mixed up and only interferes with my work. There's one of us, young Ben Tirosh— you know, the fellow who plays the sadist—he keeps asking him questions all day long. He asked him about the handkerchiefs too, so Boulanger told him that a man sees more in life if he doesn't see a thing. 'Excuse me, Boulanger,' I said to him through the girl who speaks French, 'with all due respect, do you really know what you are saying?' So he answered: 'Why does one have to understand everything, Monsieur Podmenitzki? Can you perhaps understand the birds?' "

"There certainly is something in that."

"Of course. A friend of my wife's has got a big parrot which speaks whole sentences, but it's really hard to understand him. Though he is a very old parrot and was sick last winter and keeps scratching himself all the time . . ."

Just then an old lady of noble mien stepped up to our table and kissed Podmenitzki with great feeling on both cheeks.

"Thank you," the old lady whispered. "Thank you, thank you, thank you."

She related in a voice trembling with emotion that she had gone to see *Specks* twice, just for the sake of that confrontation between Podmenitzki and his dying wife when she confesses to him in the coffin that the child was not really hers, but had been born to another woman. When the old lady left us she was sobbing, overwhelmed by the memory of two unforgettable evenings.

"What a pleasant, intelligent woman." Podmenitzki's gaze was following her. "But what woman in the play is she talking about?"

"The one who was raped by the goats. Your wife."

"She's my wife?"

"What, didn't you know?"

"I knew she was some sort of relative of mine in the play, but I didn't quite know on which side. Let's see . . . oh, I know what misled me; she says to me at the start of the second act, 'Alfonso, you're like a sister to me!' "

"And what do you reply to her?"

" 'Whore!' and bite her knee. So from that, how could I possibly know she's supposed to be my wife, right? Wait a moment, what's her reply? If I'm not mistaken, she asks to be shown mating rodents. What are rodents?"

"You know, mice, rats . . ."

"Just what I thought. That's my punchline. Dov Shlufer wrote that I gave a perfect impersonation of the nihilist who has found God within himself. You remember, when I crawl offstage at the end of the scene, completely dazed . . ."

"Yes, you were great, Mr. Podmenitzki! As you just looked with questioning eyes into the cruel infinite and kept silent . . ."

"No, that was only at the premiere, I had forgotten

my lines and was looking for Mundek behind the
scenes. But ever since then I say exactly what I have to
say: 'Only the dead are really alive, Zalman!' and exit.
At the Sabbath matinee there is always loud applause at
this point."

"What in fact are you trying to say with that, Mr.
Podmenitzki?"

"That they are clapping their hands."

"No, no, I mean that only the dead . . ."

"Those are the writer's lines, I'm not responsible
for them. At first we thought it was a printing error, but
the director checked the original and that's what it says
there too, so it stayed. Boulanger asked me to speak this
sentence somewhat philosophically, looking at the audience from floor level. He also allowed a fruity spit on
my way out and that is very forceful. Tamar Blumen-
feld wrote that this was a probing of the human soul, a
proof of lack of communication. And that is absolutely
true. I simply cannot carry on with Boulanger. Excuse
me, it's twelve thirty."

Yarden Podmenitzki produced a small transistor
from his pocket, placed it on the table and listened
raptly to the radio reviews. As he heard sweet praise,
an expression of unearthly bliss spread over his face and
his eyes filled with tears of happiness. For half a century
he had been mercilessly panned by the professional
critics. Now for the first time they realized how pains-
takingly he was building his personages, what a deeply
probing analysis this artist of genius employed. Or, to
quote I. L. Kunstetter, "an absolute identification to the
extent of a total blurring of partitions." At long last,
Yarden Podmenitzki has made it.

The next station in Yarden Podmenitzki's dizzying career is movie stardom. Yet he also goes on as a mainstay of his theatre, because in our little country all the stars earn is honor; the salary is no larger than that of a milkman covering his milky way. That's why our scenarios undergo plastic surgery every morning after the roll is called.

How Tangier was Saved

Allow me to introduce myself: I'm making the Israeli action film *Where Eagles Fear to Tread*, one of the most daring adventures in the history of local cinema, written and directed by me, supported by foreign capital—that is, a Government advance. The plot is based on a real-life story from my imagination: an Israeli commando unit blows up the rocket base at Tangier and returns safely to the studio, which is rather tough on the actors because they've got to cross Egypt, Libya and Algeria on foot, but for that I'm paying them a fortune.

The first scenes went off without a hitch. The commander of the unit, Yarden Podmenitzki in the part of gruff Grishka, picked his men from among some soldiers confined to barracks. He then led them through the Sahara—that is around and around Kibbutz Ein-Shahar in the Negev—for three days and three nights, till on the fourth day he finally arrived at my hut and came in and said:

"Seems I've got to get back to Tel Aviv tomorrow."

"Are you out of your mind?" I said. "You're going to get ambushed tomorrow, remember?"

"Sorry," thus Podmenitzki, "I had a call from the theatre that there's a rehearsal tomorrow morning. We're doing *Hamlet* and I'm his father's ghost, a part I've been waiting for all my life."

"D'you know that's a breach of contract?"

"I'm sure it is, but I'm a member of a collective. Be hearing from you!"

And he left for the North. I decided to go on shooting according to plan and just add a bit of dialogue to explain the commander's sudden disappearance due to rehearsals. The dialogue took place between a sergeant called Tripoli and the wireless operator:

WIRELESS OPERATOR: "We're approaching Tangier. But I don't see Grishka. Where is he?"

TRIPOLI (with an eloquent grin): "He'll be there, lad, trust you him!"

You can't trust anyone. Podmenitzki phoned that night that the collective had given him the part of the grandfather's ghost as well and that he had to write the text himself, so this week was out of the question.

"Podmenitzki," I told him curtly, "you're fired!"

He asked how much severance I'd pay, but I'd already hung up. The situation was delicate: the original plan had been for all my raiders to get back to base without any losses, but when I wrote the script I hadn't taken theatre rehearsals into account. One thing was clear now: Grishka must die. As an artistic solution, I ordered a young vulture from the production manager.

The vulture was to circle above him in the air and caw "Caw."

Podmenitzki's killing was reported by Tripoli in a brand-new scene. "They're going to pay dearly for Grishka!" Thus spoke the sergeant, raising his hand in a fearsome oath. They trudged on through the desert without much difficulty, guided by the daughter of the Bedouin sheikh, Tsipi Weinstein, who had fallen in love with Grishka—that is, with Tripoli now. The raiding party crossed the Sahara, and as they arrived at the kibbutz exhausted but in fine fighting spirit, over the brow of the hill there appeared the figure of Grishka running and shouting: "Wait! The director's got a cold, I've got leave from the theatre till Tuesday."

"Too bad for you, Podmenitzki," I yelled back. "We killed you yesterday. We've already ordered a vulture!"

However, since I'd hired him at a fixed sum for the entire part, it would have been a waste not to exploit him to the full. It was therefore decided that Podmenitzki would play ghost for us as well—that is, he'd float ahead of the unit to lead them through the desert, with organ accompaniment. Actually, he'd arrived just in time, as it seemed that Tripoli hadn't come back that morning from Eilat. The much-sought actor participates, as a rule, in at least three films at once. In our case he was filming in Galilee from midnight on, then made straight for us at dawn and worked till noon, at which time a dusty jeep would rush up madly to grab him for American TV at Eilat until midnight. Now he'd vanished at some point midway—fallen asleep perhaps or something. At any rate, we had to go on without him. The medic of the commando unit, a cowherd by profession whom we'd got on loan from the kibbutz for the duration, did the job.

"Boys," he declared in a close-up, "Tripoli is no more!"

"He covered our retreat," the unit commander added. "He fought to his last bullet."

Dammit, only now did I notice that I had been left without a unit commander. After Grishka's spiritualization, the unit had been left without a single name actor, except perhaps for Tsipi Weinstein, but she was the sheikh's daughter.

The new scene was very impressive: Tsipi stripped at dawn and informed the unit: "I'm a marine commando sergeant, I've taken over command!"

It was good to feel we hadn't been left leaderless for even a single yard, but we still needed to solve the problem of the father, the noble Bedouin sheikh himself. Therefore he, too, tore the "keffiyeh" off his head and introduced himself to the warriors: "Captain Lollik Tof of Jerusalem, counter-espionage. Follow me!"

All these momentous metamorphoses just for one Tripoli snoring away at some filling station somewhere in the country. Anyhow, the ranks were filled once more and the new captain strode lightly at the head of his unit beneath the burning desert sun. That evening the idiot had a fever: sunstroke.

"Malaria!" I decided. "Carry him on a stretcher!"

The medic-cowherd and the wireless operator carried him for one full shooting day, and in the evening they told me that it was too much for them—the captain's heavy and he eats all day.

"Right," I said, "but what'll we do with him?"

The two of them lowered their eyes, then threw me a wordless look and I saw death in it. I agreed to the drastic solution. I gave the chief electrician a blanket and a stick; after all, he had been a Bedouin sheikh in the original text. He climbed a hill and in a marvelous distance shot he felled the captain with a single sniper's bullet.

The sergeant threw herself on her father's body. That is, she would have thrown herself if Tsipi could have been found.

"Miss Weinstein!" The production manager scurried through camp. "You've got a new scene on, Miss Weinstein!"

In a while the truth came to light: Tsipi had joined the Carmon folk-dance troupe. I could feel it in my bones—she too wouldn't see another sun come up around here.

She fully deserved her punishment: Tsipi had got an offer from the well-known dance troupe and escaped from location to Haifa, to take part in the last two rehearsals before the troupe went off on a world tour. In my film she fell off the Red Rock. I couldn't show the actual falling because she was busy rehearsing in Haifa, as you will remember, so we only heard screams and the commando cowherd entered the tent and blurted:

"She didn't suffer much. Her last words were— Tangier . . ."

Here the wireless operator made a remark which in my view was cynical: that Tangier was located in Spain, with whom we maintained good relations. I threw an icy glance at this third-rate actor whom I was paying ridiculously high daily wages, and saw him blanch. I did a beautiful funeral scene for wayward Tsipi, because funerals are the easiest thing in the movies, you can do them even without actors. Grishka's ghost delivered the eulogy I had written on my knee right there.

After Tsipi's funeral, Grishka took me aside. "I've been thinking of this part the whole time," he told me gravely. "Don't you think that from a purely dramatic viewpoint I ought to be buried beneath the desert sands, like some new Moses to whom it was not given to step—"

"Podmenitzki," I said, "what's this about?"

"Sir," thus Podmenitzki, "I feel like dying."

"Why?"

"My son is graduating from nursery school tomorrow morning at ten, and I promised I'd be there. Let me die tonight and I'll always remember you for it."

"Maybe you can tell me who's going to take Tangier if everybody dies on me?" I yelled. "I'll sue the lot of you!"

"The child," observed Podmenitzki, "has learned a poem by heart specially for the party."

"Drop dead!"

Which is just what happened: by force of circumstance Grishka's ghost stepped on a mine and died. After his sudden departure for the nursery school, I felt the blood go to my head, and a strange passion took me in its grip when my glance spotted the wireless-operator-on-daily-wages who had hidden himself, trembling all over, behind a rusty barrel. My eyes opened in an icy stare, and the wireless operator retreated behind it to a far corner of the tent.

"No," he whispered, "you can't do that to me
. . . I've got two days coming to me according to
the contract . . . I'm still young, I want to live!
Noooo . . . !"

I had him die of thirst in the heart of the desert. A
gruesome death, but anyone who's going to quote trade-
union laws chapter and verse to me won't get any pity
here. Only the commando cowherd was left now.

"Tangier!" In a low-angle shot he pointed at the
kibbutz water tower and shouted to himself: "Follow
me!"

At this point, within an inch of the conquest of the
rocket base, we were rudely interrupted by the kibbutz
secretariat. They stopped the commando cowherd in
the middle of his lone charge and demanded that he get
back to the cowshed on the double, as two cows with
swollen bellies were expecting him.

"Gentlemen," I pleaded with the secretariat, "at
least let him depart honorably!"

A snake bit him in the leg and I myself, dressed in
the uniform of a U.N. officer, paid him final respects at
the resplendent funeral rites attended, besides myself,
by the kibbutz cook, who had a day off. I even added a
couple of cannon volleys in the final mixing. It turned
out quite an impressive occasion:

"They have fallen," I eulogized my contract-
breaking actors, "but they knew what they wanted!"

On top of the hill Grishka's ghost stood at attention, because the kindergarten teacher had moved the
party to the weekend. The vulture, high up in the air,
summed up the whole matter with a few impressive
caws.

While cutting the film I changed its title from *Where Eagles Fear to Tread* to *The Ghost Commando*. The U.N. officer, as played by me, remained the main character in the film. A number of professional critics who viewed the first working copy cried like babies during my whole action film. They said that the fact that not one of them makes it to the desired goal has a grim human documentary value which, notwithstanding a certain pacifistic tendency, is suffused with great humanitarian significance lending my work a universal appeal *par excellence*. They've got something there. I'd been thinking of that myself.

❦ *Out of solidarity with our movie stars, the Israeli movie public is made up of inveterate latecomers. Frequently they steal the show with their brilliant performance, given against a backdrop of stereophonic paper-bag rustling. The slogan of the hour:* If you can't join them, beat them!

A Cinematic Enigma

We were sitting in the second house, enjoying the subtitles on Sophia Loren's body, when suddenly there was a commotion in the fourth row behind us, and after a great deal of creaking and sorry-sorry-sorry-sorries a four-man party of latecomers settled down there. Then one of the settlers remarked in a deep and emotion-laden voice:

"You may say what you like, but no one would ever have expected Gershon Messinger to do a thing like that to us."

"That's right," a woman sitting next to him answered. "I am no longer a child, but I really would never have believed Gershon Messinger capable of this!"

"Why did Gershon Messinger do it?" a third voice asked. "And to us of all people, why?"

The question began to puzzle me as well. Really, why had Gershon Messinger done it? I tried with all my might to take my mind off this problem and concentrate on Miss Loren's divine playing, but Gershon Messinger's poison was already acting within me.

"If anybody else had done it, all right," a fourth voice said. "But Gershon Messinger of all people!"

"And to us!"

By that time all the electronic particles in my brain were tuned to Gershon Messinger. I closed my eyes to be more relaxed and accessible to the dastardly act perpetrated. Daring combinations chased each other in my brain until in the end I felt literally ashamed. It was a rather enigmatic situation, though clearly the center and possibly crucial aspect was this: why was it Gershon Messinger of all people who had shocked them so with his behavior? After clarifying this problem, we could proceed to the untangling of the other points—namely, why was it to them of all people that Gershon Messinger ought not to have done whatever he had done, rather than, say, to me; and why Gershon Messinger and not Shai Stockler or what at the time seemed even more feasible, Eli Binder?

I should have been most grateful for even the slightest clue regarding this vital problem, but the group knew only too well how to keep a secret. Small wonder, then, that I could no longer control myself, and when one of the participants again wondered how it was possible that Gershon Messinger of all people could be such a disappointment, I turned around and yelled:

"Gershon Messinger is absolutely on the ball!"

The toughest of the group jumped up to lodge a corporeal protest at my intervention, but at this fateful moment the whole audience started shouting.

"Gershon Messinger is one hundred percent right!" the crowd roared. "You deserve it from Gershon

Messinger! Hands off Gershon Messinger! Long live Gershon Messinger! Shut up!"

It was further proof, if proof were needed, that, in spite of all the conflicts that separate us, in an emergency the whole nation is as solidly united as a block of steel.

❧ *It is a well-known fact that people are not impressed by trees which have grown over the years and were never out of their sight. This, of course, is a brilliant paradigm for our Jewish State, which has grown practically on our knees from baby to young adulthood. "The State, that's me," the Israeli father-citizen therefore says and addresses the Government: "Hey, son, could you spare a tenner until tomorrow?"*

Raising the Bank

"Hello, may I speak to Mr. Horowitz?"

"Speaking."

"Is that Mr. Horowitz, Governor of the Bank of Israel?"

"Speaking."

"This is Stucks."

"Who?"

"Stucks the plumber. Mr. Horowitz, I'm in a mess."

"I beg your pardon?"

"The economic crisis is killing me, Mr. Horowitz. I was always an honest man, you can ask the contractors I work with, Stucks is the symbol of reliability, Stucks is a rock. But now we got the slowdown and I'm so nervous because of the general situation that I started raising the bank."

"What bank?"

"The bank with Wechsler. We play poker every

night. Yesterday, for instance, the bank was IL400, I held three kings, so I said to myself: 'We got unemployment, recession, so why shouldn't the fourth king come in, right?' But Wechsler said: 'You're 400, and I raise you another 600!' I went and took out the advance I had received from Steiner & Co., IL2,000, they had left with me for pipes. I had to, since I was holding three kings . . ."

"Why are you telling me all this, Mr. Stucks?"

"This is a public matter, Mr. Horowitz, you'll see in a minute. I raised the bank to IL2,000 and then, what do you know? Wechsler had three aces! All the money went down the drain. I'm telling you, the Government is creating such an atmosphere here that a man can no longer think clearly."

"Two thousand pounds are not the world."

"Yes, but that happened only yesterday. I made withdrawals in other games as well. I dipped into all the advances the contractors gave me."

"How much?"

"Twelve thousand pounds."

"Very nice. And what do the contractors say?"

"They don't know yet. As a matter of fact, that's why I'm calling you, Mr. Horowitz. There's still a chance, it's not yet too late."

"What's to be done, Mr. Stucks?"

"First of all, we'll have to let things calm down. If the Governor of the Bank of Israel doesn't want scandal, there won't be any scandal. It's a matter of state, Mr. Horowitz: I'm well known in the neighborhood for my honesty. If it becomes known that I pinched the money, they'll all say: Hell, if even Stucks got into hot water, it's the end of the world! It will lower morale to freezing point. Do you want to see all of Tel Aviv migrate, Mr. Horowitz? Show some sense of responsibility, for goodness' sake!"

"Am I responsible for your business deals?"

"But I was holding three kings!"

"Sorry, old man, you'll have to get out of this by yourself!"

"I thought of that, too, Mr. Horowitz, but it's no use. My shop is insured for only IL6,000 and now in winter there could be a sudden cloudburst and the fire would go out. On the other hand, if you'd only tell the contractors that you are personally responsible for everything, that would make a great difference. Otherwise there will be a terrible stink—scandals, lawsuits, you know. Did you ever see Steiner when he loses his temper? His face gets beet red, the veins stand out on his neck and he starts squinting, he looks frightening. What sort of impression will it make?"

"You ought to have thought of that before."

"I didn't ask your advice, Horowitz, I asked for help! If you insist, I'll register the shop in your name or in your wife's name, only give me IL15,000 as a tranquilizer."

"You said 12,000 didn't you?"

"We're playing on Saturday . . ."

"This is insolence, my boy!"

"Insolence, shminsolence, I got into hot water! So what? Things like that happen! That's what we got a government for, that's why we pay taxes, so that in such cases it should prevent panic among the population. Just think, dear Mr. Horowitz, what will happen if nine scared contractors throw themselves on me and ask for their money back! You'll see, they'll even beat up the cops! The press will lick their chops, you know those boys! Just to make people angry, why should you?"

"But—"

"Do you want me to get converted?"

"No, of course not—"

"Then send me money tomorrow morning by the first armored car you can find, if possible in fifty-pound notes."

"How are you going to refund the money?"

"Do I have to refund it? I thought this was a subsidy."

"What next?"

"All right, you've got me against the wall. On Sunday I'll refund the lot. I won't raise the bank on Saturday unless I hold four kings."

"That's not a solution, Mr. Stucks!"

"All right, four aces."

🌺 *Even today we are a very young country, and there-fore we have not yet become accustomed to the situa-tion, encouraging in itself, where every Jewish boy may one of these days become Prime Minister. It's not sur-prising, then, if the demand is extremely high. Not for the job itself, but for the pleasure of resigning. This author does it right away.*

Count Me Out

Comment on the Premiership is proliferating lately at such a rate that it looks as if, except for the Prime Minister, everybody has had his say on the subject. What all the parties have in view—so we understand— is the end of the century, when Mrs. Meir will have fin-ished her tour of duty. In the meantime, it might not be a bad idea to issue a tender worded as follows:

"State of Israel invites applications for position of Prime Minister. Offers in Yiddish to be submitted to the Trade Union Executive Committee."

Small wonder, then, if this author, too, sometimes asks himself whether he shouldn't give the idea some se-rious thought. After all, we aren't so young either, and besides there isn't in us a glimmer of that leadership which could disturb the status quo. Qualifications-wise, we are definitely a political candidate, but to our great regret it won't work after all. The job is not for us.

We simply don't want to be Premier.

The job bristles with all sorts of nuisances of which

we want no part. Just one example: In all our documents it says: "Profession—writer." Now, who has the strength to run from office to office to have that changed to "Premier"? Then we'd have to see every show that was produced under our patronage and if we fell asleep, they'd wake up our aide-de-camp at once and ask him to nudge us. And what is most deterring: "we'd have to dye our hair white and celebrate our sixty-ninth birthday and that's a horrible thought at our age.

To say nothing of personal relations. Knowing the Old Man as we do, we realize that after no more than two months he would be telling everybody we were just one big, fatal mistake. "He may be a fair yarn-spinner," Ben Gurion would say, "but he sure makes a rotten Prime Minister." What do we need that for? And at the cinema, knowing our seed-chewing riff-raff, we are sure they would applaud what's-his-name, Dayan, and grudgingly give us only a hand-clap or two, and we wouldn't enjoy that. And all the ministers would wish us every morning a long and happy life, and Abba Eban would address us in Mandarin Hebrew—no, boys, it's not for us, we feel shivers running down our spine.

Nor could we call Ambassadors "Your Excellency" and keep a straight face. And if President Nixon asked us during our intimate talk: "Say, Ephraim, are you thinking at all of ever getting out of Jerusalem?" we wouldn't know what to reply, because we blush if we have to lie in English. For the same reason, at economic conferences we would be unable to make speeches about impending prosperity. And if somebody has to strive toward the improvement of relations with the Soviet Union, we are not the right man for the job, good people—it's Fidel Castro you want. And how could we congratulate the President of Bolivia on his happy recovery when we don't know him, and anyway where is Bolivia?

Kindly leave us alone, will you?

We don't want to nip our tender family life in the bud for the sake of that Premiership. The little woman, for instance, would have to spread her patronage over the war against juvenile delinquency and things like that, and even now there is never enough fruit in the house. Once she started patronizing delinquents, the refrigerator would be empty. Nor do we feel like talking for an hour and twenty-six minutes with the Belgian Queen Mother. Even Mrs. Bialazurkevitz we can hardly stand, but at least we can always simply walk out on her, because she is only a mother, not a queen. And why should we have to lecture at the World Conference of Hadassah Women, trying to charm the delegates, when as a matter of fact we only like young chicks and not females whose vital statistics are 93–93–93? Nor do we want next to our bed a red telephone with the hot line to Party Headquarters. We want to sleep quietly at night.

And if we won at the football pools, everybody would immediately smell a rat. Only one thing draws us to the Premiership: we are dying to win literary prizes. On the other hand, who would enjoy seeing his name smeared on the wall, adorned with unflattering epithets? We know our own weaknesses, why rub them in in public? Also, we are used to speaking our own mind —why would we all of a sudden need an advisor to guide our every step?

No, it won't do. We don't want to kiss the chubby cheeks of little babies giving us flowers on the occasion of something or other. We love only our own children —the others have parents who should take care of them. And we won't be godfather to any tenth child because we faint whenever they start doing that thing at the brith mila. We feel no urge at all to talk to simple people about this year's harvest: deep in our heart we are against rain because of the mud on our doorstep. And last but not least, the very thought that from time to time we'd have to mount to the Torah in Brooklyn to the cheers of thousands of donors—the very thought makes us wake up screaming at night.

And all the time they'd keep guessing who would be the next Prime Minister while we were still Prime Minister.

No, folks, we are most grateful to all who offered us the job, but we are not yet ripe for the task. For the time being you'll have to make do without us. We recommend our wife for a trial period.

The Night Our Hair Turned Gray

The premiere was over and we had duly stepped backstage and congratulated the architects of victory, then assembled in front of the theatre to talk things over in earnest. The mood was jubilant, because the show was obviously a bomb.

Then Kunstatter asked, I clearly remember him asking, "Say, how about a bite?"

We reacted with uninhibited glee. Somebody mentioned the new Balalaika restaurant with its cultivated French cuisine. Though we realized that prices would be rather high at such a posh eatery, the show had been so enjoyably lousy that we decided this was no time for penny-pinching.

It was quite a place—the walls covered with red rugs, intimate candlelight, the ceiling of wood and the waiters from southern France. They pulled up six tables for us, and only then did we notice that no less than twenty people had come along, among them a number of complete strangers. This is an almost unavoidable situation—people on the fringe of show business always follow the celebrities wherever they go.

We ordered the entree and the main dish, though the price list confirmed our worst fears. But the food was glorious, the wine heady, the conversation sparkling, so what the hell?

I had just finished the oven-baked chops when the little one gently poked me in the ribs.

"Ephraim," she whispered, "look!"

My glance swept the length of the table. Strange, I mused, several chairs had become vacant. Those who had sat in them had apparently finished their meal and vanished. Altogether, twelve were left, including ourselves. "They fall who go first," the old military adage says, but there is no intimation anywhere that they have to pay before going.

I looked around searchingly. The headwaiter in his gleaming tuxedo was standing in a strategic corner, raising his bushy eyebrows, taking notes.

I returned my glance to my fellow diners: there was a certain look of dejection about them. A hidden fear was flickering in their eyes, a fear which cannot be fully expressed in words, but if pressed one could read: "Who's going to pay for this?"

The next head count showed only ten celebrants left. Another couple had left under the cloak of the intimate lighting. Conversation dragged, unbearable tension took over. No one dared look his fellow in the eye, gears were audibly clanking as we computed the exorbitant prices.

Gradually, glances focused on Kunstatter.

From a strictly moral point of view, it was only fair that he should pay. After all, it had been his invitation, his stupid idea to have a bite. What had been his exact words? Let's see: "Come on, friends," he had said, "come and have dinner with me," or perhaps he had even said, "Be my guests tonight, folks," or words to that effect. Without any doubt he was our man. He was also honest. He would pay.

All eyes were on Kunstatter.

Kunstatter finished his meal with disconcerting calm and ordered coffee. We held our breath, our nostrils flared. If Kunstatter now turned to us and asked "Coffee, anyone?" that would establish his responsibility, his host status and his willingness to bear the consequences. But Kunstatter sipped his coffee with a noncommittal face and talked to his wife.

Meanwhile a few more rats had fled the sinking ship. The passenger list had shrunk to seven lost souls.

Who's going to pay?

The lively conversation had long ago fizzled out. Now and then we exchanged a few grunts about Suez and the latest divorces in town, but this was just a pretext for passing to the "everybody fend for himself" stage. Now every additional desertion would increase the danger of having to pay. It was obvious that all those left were alert to the danger.

Then a terrible thing happened.

One of the hostages, Ben-Zion Ziegler, rose with demonstrative nonchalance and said:

"Excuse me, I must call the office."

And with measured steps he escaped from our field of vision. Cold sweat ran down our brows. Only then did we realize that he had come alone, without his wife, thereby enjoying superior mobility.

Ben-Zion Ziegler never returned.

Weeks later, eyewitnesses related that he had indeed entered a phone booth and, upon leaving it, had languidly waved toward us and passed through the main entrance. No one had seen him waving. When did he wave? And what if he had waved?

Who's going to pay?

More dropouts increased the tension. Personally, I cursed the recklessness which had made the little one and myself sit with our backs to the waiters, unable to see what they were plotting in the background. This weakened my position to the point of making it eminently dangerous. Any moment now, the headwaiter would show up at our back . . . the bill under a napkin on the plate . . . and I had no room for maneuver. Terrible!

"Excuse me." Kunstatter suddenly jumped to his feet, consulting his watch with great concern. "The baby-sitter . . . !"

And before we could gather our wits he left with his wife. Engineer Glick rose as if intending to shout something after him, but not a word left his gasping throat. Unmitigated panic broke out. Kunstatter had been our last hope; after his desertion only three hapless couples were left: the Glicks, the Bar Honigs and us.

I looked behind. The waiter was standing in his corner, never letting us out of his sight. Never in my life had I seen such bushy eyebrows.

How much could the bill be? Twenty lamb chops . . . Goodness!

Mrs. Bar Honig started jabbering Polish with her husband. Even without an interpreter, we all understood what the shouting was about. What's more, we answered categorically, albeit mutely:

"I'm not willing either, you witch!"

The main thing was not to give in! The little one, chalk-white, gripped my damp hand under the table. It's a good feeling to know that in life's critical moments one is not alone. That gave me the strength to concentrate on our plight. Because it was clear that from now on the battle was to the death. One careless step and you are finished. So, just don't lose your head, hold out, old boy! Whoever shows the first sign of wavering or inner weakness, whoever gave the slightest hint to the waiter—he'll pay the bill.

Before the mind's eye there arose tragic cases in which innocent people had paid at the end of the meal for the whole gathering, just because they had lifted a hand to chase away a fly. In such cases the waiter swoops down straight on the signaler and discreetly hands him the bill. No signals, no moves! The reader probably knows those horrible moments when several couples are sitting at the table and the waiter stands within range with his numerologic plate, his eyes roaming left and right in the oppressive silence. One ages years in such moments. If you just shake your head, move your hand ever so slightly toward your pocket, you've had it. You pay. These are elementary rules. So keep cool!

The time was 3:00 A.M. For the last two hours we had been all by ourselves in the restaurant, completely isolated from the outside world. But no one dared propose that we leave, because he who called the waiter would also have to pay the bill.

But what's that?

Suddenly I felt that my wife's hand was turning ice-cold. In a flash I decoded her message. Bar Honig and Engineer Glick suddenly started talking with disgusting eagerness. They talked with alacrity and cut into each other's words. The blood drained from my head. I felt that the moment of truth had come. Somewhere in the recesses of the restaurant the waiter had started moving toward me . . .

I had only a few seconds left. My brain worked feverishly. Clearly, they were isolating me in preparation for the clash. The waiter would come, see that I was the only accessible man at the table, and naturally . . .

I closed my eyes and decided to try a finesse.

There was no choice. Only by bluffing could I hope to save my skin. I would try to make the two believe that I was willing and ready to settle the bill, and thus gain their confidence, so that at the last moment, when my hand was already in my pocket, one of them would swallow the bait and, prompted by his European manners, would make a gesture and mumble: "Hey, let me do that." Whereupon I would immediately retreat— "Please!"—and leave him with the bill! This is called the Haifa Gambit because it is said to have been devised by a Haifa industrialist two years ago on New Year's Eve.

I therefore turned round and called out loudly: "Waiter! The bill!"

Bar Honig and Glick stopped talking, pleasantly

surprised, and dropped back, exhausted. I pulled out my wallet with a sweeping movement so as to dispel any doubt in their hearts and counted up to three: 1–2–3. But tonight Haifa failed dismally—no one swallowed the bait. They kept mum as a shoal of fish. Their noses quivered slightly and their eyes were downcast. That's all. Engineer Glick even managed a sadistic grin. I hated them.

I lifted the napkin with two fingers and peeped:

"*160 . . . pounds . . .*"

"Only sign, please," the waiter said. "Mr. Kunstatter put everything on his account before he left."

❧   *Modern literature has practically exhausted all the possible variations in the game of love: man with man, woman with woman, man with woman (?), old man with Lolita, old woman with Pinocchio, young girls with old men, old women with old women, etc. Herewith our modest contribution to world literature under the influence of our country's unstable climate.*

Madelaine

At dusk, as the surrounding orange groves resounded to the laughter of the jackals and the wind brought billowing sand clouds from the desert, Shultheiss showed up on my doorstep. I was glad to see him because he hadn't been at my place for quite a while. He had not changed, was the same suave, well-dressed Shultheiss: distinguished, intellectual, yet his eyes were rather sad, I thought. He sat down in the garden and quietly sipped Jordan water.

"I must speak to you," he said after a while.

"Please, that's why we are here."

"I hesitated for a long time over whether I had the right to share my secret with anyone. After all, I am a senior Government official and must safeguard my reputation. But I cannot keep the affair to myself any longer."

I poured him another glass of Jordan. He gulped it down.

"I don't know where to start. You've known me

for a long time, you know that I am a well-balanced, healthy person enjoying the full confidence of his superiors."

"That's right."

"Yes, that's how I appear to the casual observer. But in fact, believe me, I am as lonely as a man on the moon. I am a bachelor, somehow I never found a suitable mate, I live by myself, quite alone. To be quite frank, I've longed all my life for a little warmth. But I never found it until Madelaine came into my life."

Shultheiss stared into the air for a while, then continued:

"You know, sometimes one doesn't even realize that fate is knocking at one's door. On that day, I did not even dream . . ."

He pulled out a little notebook.

"It was November third last year."

"So the liaison has lasted for six months now!"

Yes. I woke up shivering in the morning and called the doctor, who found that I had the flu and prescribed something. My neighbor took the prescription to the pharmacy and returned with a box. I opened it and found a rubber flask."

"A hot-water bottle?"

"Yes, made of pink rubber, local manufacture, with a threaded plug. Nothing special. So help me, I am ashamed."

"But why?"

"After all, these are intimate things and I don't like talking about them. When first I filled it up with hot water I definitely remember it was pouring outside and freezing cold in the room. I placed the bottle next to my body and, believe it or not, for the first time in my life I felt a little warmth around my heart. For the first time I was not alone. Can you understand me?"

"Of course."

"It's difficult to put this into words. There it is lying next to you, this warm, soft object, and its only task is to make your life pleasant. You can't imagine how grateful I was to Madelaine."

"I beg your pardon?"

"That's what I named her from the very beginning, Madelaine. Why Madelaine? So help me, I don't know. I felt I had to call her that. And from then on, storms no longer bothered me—I had Madelaine with me under my blanket. Do you find this odd?"

"Well, many people use hot-water bottles."

"You've got to understand me. If my feet are cold, I place her there. Pains in my hip, Madelaine soothes the pain. And if I feel like it, I can even place her on my belly. Believe me, the possibilities are practically unlimited. And Madelaine always stays modest, loyal, devoted, all she asks for is a little hot water. For quite a long time I didn't dare to confess it even to myself, but now there is not much sense in denying it . . ."

"Are you in love with her?"

"Perhaps," he whispered. "It has not yet crystallized. I think I am a typical Pygmalion case. I am sure you know the beautiful legend about the English linguist who fell in love with the statue of Aphrodite. Believe me, I see the situation clearly. Frequently I ask myself: How is it possible for an intelligent, serious, adult man to be crazy about a plain little rubber flask when there are so many bigger and more expensive hot-water bottles? But I need only her, little Madelaine . . . Frankly, I am even a little jealous of her. I simply can't help it."

"Did she ever betray you?"

"Yes, once!"

Shultheiss nervously lighted a cigarette.

"It was not her fault, only the circumstances were to blame. Early this year Madelaine developed a leak. In my madness, I wanted her to be even warmer and filled her up with such hot water that it burned her sides. You can imagine how desperate I was. I took her right away to the best rubber specialist in town—but a terrible thing happened. In the evening I went to fetch Madelaine, whereupon that crook pressed into my hand a completely strange container. The miserable jerk had switched bottles. I don't think he had done it on purpose, but that's no excuse. I rushed all over town until midnight before I found Madelaine . . . in a fat feather merchant's . . . bed . . ."

"In the act?"

Shultheiss could only nod wordlessly.

"Since then I have never let her out of my sight. On the other hand, I am worried sick that her ulcers may start up again. Frequently I wake up in a sweat, having dreamed that she was leaking. My fear reached such a pitch that I even sought out a marriage consultant. He examined me and declared that there was only one solution: buy another bottle, because only a new bottle could lessen the morbid influence Madelaine has on me."

"Did you buy one?"

"I did. But ever since it lies unused in a drawer. I

know that the law entitles me to keep two bottles, but it certainly doesn't force me to use them, does it?"

"No, I guess it doesn't."

"Look. Madelaine and I are joined for life. There is nothing one can do about it."

"Let me congratulate you. It's only rarely that one meets such a deep, human relationship."

"Hang on. I am sorry, but I have not yet told you the reason for my visit. Difficult though it is, I have to admit that a certain circumstance clouds our happiness. It's most embarrassing to talk about it, but, you see, these bottles don't keep the heat for more than four or five hours and then—how can I say it?"

"They become frigid?"

"Thank you for relieving me of the need to say so, because in spite of my sentiments toward Madelaine I have to admit that there is almost nothing more unpleasant to the touch than a cold rubber bottle. So, when at dawn, half asleep, I feel that cold abomination on my feet, I simply kick it out of my bed."

"No!"

"It's beastly, isn't it? And then in the morning when I get up and see the poor dear . . . lying on the floor . . . limp and exhausted . . ."

Shultheiss sobbed.

"I am so ashamed," he whispered. "This is a terrible tragedy. As long as she is hot, I cling to her, but as soon as she cools, I throw her away like a rag. It would never have occurred to me that I could be so cruel."

"So don't kick her."

"But when she is so cold! You know in what situation this puts me? Mornings, when I find her on the floor, I beg her forgiveness on my knees and promise Madelaine that never . . . never . . . never again . . . And next morning again I . . . kick her out . . ."

Shultheiss was in a state of collapse.

"Please help me," he whined. "What shall I do?"

"Fill her up again with hot water at dawn."

"You think so?" Shultheiss raised his eyes from the ground. "Perhaps you are right. At three thirty I'll refill Madelaine. That should restore our bliss."

He left with uncertain steps. I looked after him thoughtfully. Hot stuff for a movie.

❦ *Is the pioneering spirit still alive? This question exercises our population between banquets and parties. Nor is this a trifling question, since it is very difficult to get rich in old age and at the same time stay young and poor.*

How the Mafia Began

The idea was Shmuel's. We were sitting in his room, Haim, Nehama and I, cursing the whole unholy mess.

"The country's cultural situation is catastrophic," Haim remarked. "Youth swamps the cinemas and gobbles up those cheap American magazines. Hebrew literature has reached an impasse."

We all agreed. Impotent fury and an ardent desire to help fought within us, with changing luck.

In the end Nehama jumped up. "Talk, talk, talk!" she burst out. "Let's act! We're young, beautiful and strong. We still believe in a better, truer and exquisite future. Let's save Israel's cultural life, so there should be some point to our lives."

Our tawny, satiny cheeks flushed with pleasure; in our sparkling eyes hope flashed like summer lightning, and our slender figures straightened up.

"We'll set up a little circle," I proposed. "We'll gather around us all the ardent, selfless forces who still care about the country's spiritual make-up."

"That's it!" thus Shmuel. "Long live the Circle of

Friends of Hebrew Culture!"

We talked on into the wee hours about our great new enterprise. We decided to rent premises which we would make habitable through selfless work, so that it would become a small but intimate oasis for every true and young-in-heart friend of the arts. We further decided to have highly refined literary evenings, receipts to be devoted to supporting young talent. Our spirits soared to a climax and stayed right there.

At dawn, instead of going to bed, we started looking for adequate premises so that the holy cause should suffer no delay. And indeed we located a nice little basement, but the owner, a Greek fertilizer merchant, would not lease it to us.

"Who are you?" he said. "What are you? What kind of circle are you? Where's your agreement?"

We broke into loud guffaws. Agreement? Ridiculous! We didn't need any agreement. The common aim and our fervent love of Hebrew culture created a much closer community of interest among us than any silly piece of paper. But the Greek insisted that he would deal only with a corporate body, otherwise he would never know from whom to claim the unpaid rent. Willy-nilly, we decided to have a reputable lawyer draft some sort of contract so as to get these stupid formalities out of the way.

The lawyer, a certain Dr. Shay-Sonnenschein, received us in his office. He impressed us most favorably, except that his office had in its previous incarnation been the root cellar of the house and consequently had no windows.

"I'm so glad to make your acquaintance," Dr. Shay-

Sonnenschein said. "As a matter of fact, who are you, and what's all this about?"

"We're young, sir, and still have ideals," thus Shmuel. "We'd like to place all our strength in the service of the country's spiritual renaissance, so that future generations may enjoy the fruits of our selfless and large-scale cultural activity."

The lawyer nodded. "I see. You desire to set up a so-called 'non-profit, unlimited liability society.'"

"Profits are quite irrelevant," Haim remarked. "I'm sure we'll show a loss, despite our voluntary work."

"You can never tell," the lawyer said. "Now you are still unsophisticated and young, but in ten years' time you may well think quite differently. I suggest you set up a so-called 'Ottoman Society.'"

"All right," we said and started to leave, but Dr. Shay-Sonnenschein detained us, saying that a number of details had to be clarified.

"First of all, I must specify in the statutes how the society will be dissolved."

A hot rage seized us. What was he talking about? Why the hell should we dissolve when we could hardly wait to be established? So we told the jurist to forget about dissolving.

"That's not as you think," the lawyer explained. "Now you're still young, but who knows, in ten years' time you might hate each other's guts. That's why it is advisable to clarify these ticklish problems right from the beginning. I propose that a general assembly should unanimously decide the liquidation."

"As you like."

"Right. Now, how will the property of the disintegrating enterprise be distributed?"

"Come, come, what property?"

"You just wait and see what's going to happen in ten years' time! I propose that the members of the general assembly should receive equal shares of the movable property and real estate. In case of litigation an elected arbitration board decides."

"What sort of litigation?"

"You'll see. Sorry, but that's how it is. Now you are still young, but you won't always be young. By the way, we also have to decide whom you'll admit as members in the society."

"Anybody blessed with genuine, constructive creativity."

"That isn't a legal definition. In such cases the governing body will have to decide."

"What governing body?"

"According to Ottoman legislation, a three-man governing body must head the society."

"Too bad, because there are four of us."

"Then one is superfluous."

We gaily laughed at each other. This was ridiculous.

"Nonsense," Haim remarked. "So let's say that Ephraim won't be a member of the 'governing body' . . ."

We burst out laughing. All of us were furious for having to waste our time on such trifles while our vocation was beckoning to us. In addition, I was also furious that they had dropped me from the governing body. Why me? This was not nice. I would remember their attitude.

"So we've set up the governing body," Dr. Shay-Sonnenschein remarked. "Now let's decide how to remove unsuitable members from the Society."

"I beg your pardon—"

"Look, I don't mean now. But in ten years' time you may find that you simply cannot get along with one of your members, or that he is a crook or something, and you want to kick him out."

I clearly remember that they all looked at me. Why at me and only at me?

"I suggest," the lawyer said, "that a member should be removed only by the unanimous vote of the board."

"Out of the question." I raised my voice. "I don't trust the board. Only the general assembly can decide."

"Convening the general assembly would be too cumbersome," Shmuel protested. "So, in effect we won't be able to get rid of anybody."

"If, for instance, we kicked out Shmuel," I raised a hypothetical legal problem, "would we have to pay him something, sir?"

"The board will have to decide on that as well."

"Out of the question!" Nehama flared up. "If, for instance, they make my life hell, I won't argue with the bastards. My compensation must be fixed in advance!"

"Why not?" Dr. Shay-Sonnenschein said. "There is room for everything in the statues. Perhaps, to make tax fraud easier, we'll say that the departing member gets six months' salary in lieu of severance pay."

"What salary?"

"Whatever you decide. Remember, the Society will be non-profit, so you will have to distribute all profits among yourselves."

"Now really, those few pounds?"

"Right now it's a few pounds. In ten years' time it could be hundreds of thousands. After all, you will have a snack bar on the premises. You can also rent them out for bar mitzvoth. You could organize musical teas. Sabbath evening dances are very popular. With a little effort you'll get a tax exemption. The net profit can be distributed among the members in the guise of salaries."

"Not among all members," Haim proposed. "Perhaps just among the four founding members present here."

We accepted this proposal unanimously.

"As a rule, I am against admitting riff-raff to the club," Nehama opined. "We ought to charge high membership fees, so that only cultured people should join."

The lawyer served coffee. His cubicle had filled with cigarette smoke. Shmuel had distanced himself somewhat from me. Out of the corner of my eye I threw a piercing glance at this digusting opportunist.

Nehama and Haim kept whispering to each other and from time to time pointed a finger at myself or Shmuel. I made up my mind to get rid of these two snakes in the grass as soon as possible.

"What's the situation, sir," I asked the lawyer, "if it's found that one of us has a criminal record? He might bolt with our cash!"

"In that case the founding general assembly will have to be convened at once."

"And if the person in question is a spy who infiltrated our circle?" Nehama remarked and threw me a glance burning with hatred. "What is to be done with such a villain?"

"You have to hand him over to the police and elect a new board."

"And if one of us smokes hashish or runs amuck? Or is a dangerous lunatic?"

"You're quite right to ask. You will have to include in your statutes a section according to which the board will be entitled to remove without further ado sick and old people who can no longer earn their living."

"That's right," Shmuel croaked. "We don't need cripples!"

Haim, who has ulcers, grew deathly pale and grabbed a bronze paperweight. "What does the law say," he inquired, "about one of us murdering the other?"

"In case of murder, an arbitration court decides on the share to be paid to the widow. But this will do for today, I think." Dr. Shay-Sonnenschein closed the file of the Friends of Hebrew Culture. "I suggest we meet again on Friday afternoon to discuss investments, dividends and import licenses."

Shmuel was for importing mainly Swedish porno films and American glossy magazines, while I proposed importing genuine English switchblade knives. On the way out I tried not to go in front. It is unpleasant to walk the empty streets with these *mafiosi*. "So on Friday, general meeting!" Nehama remarked, and without taking leave, feeling ten years older, we dispersed. I'll get myself a submachine gun for Friday. You can never tell.

🌺 *"My best friends are Jews," the professional anti-Semite says in the Diaspora, trying to justify why he can't stand the rest. With us, because of the markedly Semitic character of our nation, the situation is somewhat different and our best enemies are our friends.*

A Friend Indeed

As a rule, I am of a rather surly disposition. To be more precise, it's not exactly surly, but perhaps I am a bit too serious. In other words, I am not childish, my mouth is not permanently contorted in a stupid grin, I am moderate in my views, simply an adult. That is, I am of a surly disposition. Yet, it so happened that on that day I was feeling on top of the world. I don't know why, maybe by mistake I had slept well, or else the humidity may have dropped and my blood pressure risen —anyway, I felt wonderful that morning. The sun was shining, the trees were in bloom, the birds were not twittering, a pleasant quiet, I was simply satisfied with myself and life in general.

Then I had a call from Shlomo, my best pal. I lifted the receiver and said: "Hello!"

"Ephraim," Shlomo answered, "what's eating you?"

"Me? Nothing is eating me."

"Ephraim," thus Shlomo, "I know you inside out. I have only to lift the receiver and hear your voice to realize at once that something is wrong with you.

What's eating you?"

"Everything's fine."

"Ephraim!"

"So help me, I don't know what you're talking about!"

"You sound terribly nervous . . ."

"I'm not nervous, but if you keep on asking me what's eating me, I'll get nervous."

"I thought it would relieve you to share your troubles with someone."

"But I'm telling you I have no troubles, damn it!"

"A good thing you can't hear your own voice. You sound completely hysterical. I only hope it's nothing serious."

"Couldn't we change the subject?"

"Do you think that would solve anything?"

"Yes!"

"All right. What are you doing tonight, why don't you drop in?"

"I will, Shlomo."

"Look, Ephraim," my pal said, slightly offended, "we could go on like that, exchanging meaningless trifles for hours on end—'Why don't you drop in?' 'I will, Shlomo'—but I was foolish enough to believe we were beyond those things. What's eating you, Ephraim?"

"If you ask just once more what I'm eating, I'll hang up!"

"You know what you said just now? Did I ask you what you are eating? Do I care what you are eating?"

"I mean, what's eating me!"

"You no longer know what you're saying. You are

completely off your bat . . ."

He sounded very convincing. His voice was calm, his manner restrained, while I stuttered like a frightened child.

"Don't take anything to heart," Shlomo continued. "Believe me, as long as you are healthy and able to walk and talk, there's no reason to be as dejected as all that. Don't give a damn, what do you care? Everybody has his ups and downs, I know you, you'll be all right in the end! The main thing: chin up, keep smiling!"

"But so help me—"

"Ephraim!"

Except for "What's eating you?" nothing upsets me so much as his saying in a deep voice ringing with sympathy: "Ephraim!" It literally gives me the heebies.

"First of all," Shlomo continued, "you must be honest with yourself. This and this happened, this and this might happen, this and this I have to do!"

"This and this and this," I mumbled and had a look in the mirror. A new face was looking at me. I had greatly aged.

"Have you seen a doctor yet?"

"Why a doctor?"

"Ephraim, I beg of you, get a grip on yourself! It's very sad to see you go to pieces like that."

"But I'm all right, you hear? Quite all right!"

Shlomo didn't answer. I assume he was fighting his tears. We are very good friends.

"Ephraim," he said in the end, hoarsely, "what's the matter?"

I didn't answer.

"Ephraim, don't do anything rash," his voice came

over the line. "You're still young, at least in spirit, your whole life is still before you! Chase away those thoughts, 'What for, for whom, for goodness' sake?' Life is beautiful, don't throw it away recklessly. Ephraim . . ."

I rose to hang myself, but then changed my mind and went instead to the movies. Shlomo's voice fol-lowed me to the door:

"Ephraim! Ephraim! Why don't you answer? E-p-h-r-a-i-m!"

The above conversation took place a week ago. Last night the phone rang again.

"Hello!"

"Listen," Shlomo said, "your voice sounds strange tonight."

"Of course," I answered, "our house burned down."

"You don't say!"

"Also, a tricycle ran me down on Dizengoff Street."

"Yes?"

"Yes. And my wife ran away with an acrobat from the Bulgarian circus."

"Never mind," thus Shlomo, "it will pass. Drop in tonight if you feel like it. 'Bye."

❦ *During thousands of years of exile and persecution, Jewry locked itself in an intellectual ivory tower and neglected to develop its body. Our renewed country restored to Jewry the simple, common-fellow type, and now we are paying dearly for that gift.*

The Four Horsemen of the Apocalypse

When does a person sleep best?

According to the latest scientific report, a person enjoys his deepest sleep before 5:25 A.M. At 5:25 A.M. the average citizen is awakened, whimpering like a frightened animal, by an earthquake-like explosion. The unexpected cataclysm which throws him out of his bed is not made up of a single tone. The infernal noise sounds as if it were a variety of recorded tapes being played back at the same time: you can discern in it a sudden air raid, a buffalo stampede, a thunderstorm and a column of Centurion tanks, as well as the jungle yell of the avenging Tarzan . . . At 5:25.

Everybody reacts differently to the extra-terrestrial phenomenon. There are lodgers who dig in deeply under their pillows and pray there fervently. Others roll off their couches and dash about their bedrooms aimlessly. This writer as a rule no sooner hears the explosion than he hurls himself on his little wife, strangling her without uttering a single word, until she succeeds in turning on the bedside lamp and convincing him that he is not having a nightmare.

"How could a mere four men make such an infernal racket?" my neighbor Felix Selig asked, leaning out of the window at 5:25 A.M. "*How?*"

We watched from up there the Four Horsemen of the Apocalypse: the driver of the municipal garbage truck, the fellow who stands on the runningboard and the two individuals who drag out the garbage bins from the courtyard. At first sight they are four simple sanitation experts, but their unassuming exteriors conceal a quartet of top-flight *virtuosi* of the noise technique: the driver, for instance, drives exclusively in first gear, revving up his diesel engine to the maximum, while the bins are dragged over the largest rocks in the courtyard, amid ceaseless altercations, frequently giving the impression that the men are just about to kill each other off.

Each other?

By listening carefully, we found that there was not even a quarrel among them. They were chatting about the most common everyday subjects. According to the unwritten rules of disturbing the peace, the conversation begins only when the two toilers are dragging the bins from deep inside the courtyard, about twenty to thirty paces from the truck. They then turn back and roar in the general direction of the driver.

"Hey! Hey! Where'd you go last night, where'd you go?"

The driver sticks his head out of the window and trumpets into the rosy dawn. "Hey! We stayed at home! And you?"

"We went to the war movie, we did! It was a great movie, so help me, how they acted!"

The unfortunate neighbors who live in the rear of the house swear that the two bin-carrying individuals sometimes converse with each other two feet apart.

"Listen," they roar at the top of their lungs, "it's damn heavy today, damn heavy, right?"

"Of course it's heavy, they eat like horses on this street, they eat!"

Mrs. Kalaniot, whom fate has placed plumb on top of the bins and because of this is permanently on the verge of a nervous breakdown, tore open her window one dawn and shouted at the Horsemen: "Quiet, for goodness' sake! Quiet! Why must you be so noisy every night?"

"Night, what night?" one individual roared back pleasantly. "It's already half past five, isn't it?"

"I'll call the police!" Adalbert Toscanini joined the choir of protestors, whereupon the Four Horsemen broke into such a horse laugh that any policeman passing by would have frozen into a column of salt.

"Yeah, call one, go ahead!" they roared at Adalbert. "Where would you find a cop at five thirty, where would you find one?"

They are gay, uninhibited fellows, these municipal sanitation employees, muscular Jewish boys full of vitality, *joie de vivre* and decibels. Karl Marx would have wept for joy had he lived to see them. You get the impression that no force in the world could curb them. It's an impression borne out by fact. Take ourselves, for instance. At last week's protest meeting the neighbors entrusted me with contacting the municipal sanitation department with the aim of attenuating the matinal earthquakes. I dialed the department head and told him my tale of woe.

"You're telling me," the head replied with much feeling. "I get the same program every morning. They're driving me nuts."

In summer when all the windows were open, we forwarded a multi-signature petition to the authorities, in which we requested that the Four Horsemen of the Apocalypse be forbidden to toss the bins three yards high in the air, thereby setting off a report which at 5:30 A.M. causes multiple nerve-snappings in the neighbors. We got no reply. The Sieglers' maid, a certain Etroga, who happens to live next door to the man on the runningboard, advised us not to do anything; two Ministers had already tried to intervene, but in the end had been forced to resign and retire to a kibbutz.

The lawyer whom we consulted considered carefully the various alternatives open to us.

"Spend the weekend in Jerusalem," he advised in the end. "There the sanitation workers frequently go on strike."

So we resorted to cotton wool. We stuffed our ears with it and achieved a certain sordino effect, but the siren-like "Heys" cut through it like a hot knife through margarine.

At the last meeting Dr. Wasserlauf gave a visionary lecture. "The chronic insomnia as well as the perpetual traumatic shocks will eventually leave their imprint on our brain functions," the Doctor said. "I have no doubt whatsoever that our heirs will show the alarming signs of their parents' degeneration and that the morning trash collection will in the final analysis result in a steep decline in the intellectual level of the general population."

Before our mind's eye appeared our grandchildren fastening on us sad, reproachful looks, then disappearing with queer, goatlike hops into the dense forest. "No!" We ground our teeth. "Something has to be done, something!" Siegler quoted the famous adage: "If you can't break them, join them!" This compromise attitude was in tune with our inborn sense of decency, since it goes without saying that deep in our hearts we boundlessly admired the four trashmen who at crack of dawn were already engaged in heavy physical work while we, poor white trash that we are, went on snoring under our blankets until 5:25. It was therefore decided to try the individual psychological approach—money was no object.

On that bizarre Tuesday morning, for instance, we monitored the following broadcast.

"Hey," the runningboard man roared to the individuals, "it's getting cold, isn't it?"

"Hey!" the reply thundered back from the recesses of the yard. "Buy yourself a sweater, a sweater buy yourself."

"What sweater! What are you saying, a sweater you are saying? Where have I got a sweater, hey, hey!"

We acted without further delay. For our families, for our children's future, for Middle East peace. Out of the house sanitation fund, Mrs. Kalaniot bought a remarkable red sweater of the largest neck size and Felix Selig, accompanied by Etroga, took it to the house of the runningboard fellow. The delegation solemnly handed over the neighbors' gift, voicing the hope that the warm clothing would contribute toward the creation of a quieter atmosphere. The runningboard fellow could hardly conceal his emotion, expressed his gratitude for the nice present and promised at once to tell his closest collaborators.

Next day at 5:25 Mrs. Kalaniot was hurled out of her bed by the following roar:

"Hey!" thus the runningboard buffalo. "They bought me a sweater here, you hear what they bought?"

"They're nice folks, they are, nice!" the driver roared back into the daybreak. "They're good people, but really good!"

Then followed the ultimate explosion when the runningboard fellow, in his joy over the new sweater, hurled the bin in a daring parabola straight onto another bin precariously balanced on the fence and the two of them ricocheted onto the pavement like two stray grenades. Ever since, the hearing in my left ear is somewhat impaired. On the other hand, I sleep rather well on my right side. This is such an excellent solution that I am surprised I didn't think of it before.

❧ Anyone who crawls along one of America's highways at a speed of fifty m.p.h. risks getting a ticket. He runs the same risk here—for speeding. This is no proof of the theory of relativity, but a covert criticism of the sorry state of our highways.

The Speed Maniac

One historic evening not long ago as I headed for home in my motor vehicle, an alert traffic cop stopped me dead in my tracks and said: "License. You were speeding in a built-up area."

"Maybe," I answered. "Prove it!"

"As you like . . ."

With that the cop walked us back to a quietly pasturing police car. In it was an officer and in front of him an infernal contraption with all sorts of dials and pushbuttons. I realized at once that it was a radar instrument, that invention of the devil. So that's what they waste the taxpayers' money on!

The cop inspected my documents. "Oho! I see that you are a journalist. You ought to be an example to others instead of driving like a madman."

"I am so ashamed, officer." I duly lowered my eyes. "Now that I see you are radar-equipped, I am sorry it ever happened."

"So you confess that you drove at an excessive speed?"

"Of course I do."

"Why did you drive at an excessive speed, sir?"

"I was in a hurry," I said. "I was in a hurry."

"Why did you hurry?"

"Because the oncoming cars did not signal with their headlights that a speed-trap is ahead."

"And is that a reason to drive at an excessive speed?"

"Of course it isn't. Allow me to mention that I have been driving for the past thirteen years and this is the first time I've exceeded the speed limit."

"Is this the first time you've exceeded the speed limit or the first time you were caught?"

"The first time I exceeded the speed limit."

"If that is so, then how come for thirteen years you did not exceed the speed limit and now all of a sudden you exceeded the speed limit?"

"It just so happens that now I exceeded the speed limit. Please write out my ticket."

"You write in the newspapers. Do you know what would happen if everybody exceeded the speed limit?"

"There would be accidents."

"Would you, sir, like to cause accidents?"

"No, of course not."

"Then why did you exceed the speed limit?"

"God knows," I replied. "As a rule we pay IL20 for exceeding the speed limit, so perhaps—"

"How do you know how much one pays for speeding when you, sir, have never yet been given a ticket for speeding?"

"That's what I was told by gentlemen drivers who have been given tickets for speeding."

"Will you ever exceed the speed limit in future?"

"Yes!" I roared in a strange voice and tore off my tie. "Yes, I'll always exceed the speed limit! Always! All the time I'll espeed the ex milit! Espimilit . . ."

"All right." The cop frowned. "I would have let you off with a warning, but I am ruthless with hooligans. Here is your ticket for speeding."

❦ *In our country there is a great demand for skilled*
workers in all categories except ski instructors, chimney-
sweeps and poets. The representatives of the latter pro-
fession give proof of praiseworthy perseverance in writ-
ing thick tomes of Hebrew poetry. Some of them even
succeed in selling several editions, but for that they have
to sell their souls to the devil at cut rates and in easy
installments.

The Great Literary
Freak Show

The publisher took the manuscript out of his
drawer and said to Tolaat Shani: "I've read them."

The poet slid to the edge of his chair. "Yes?" he
whispered. "Yes?"

"Wonderful poems. I don't think anything as exquisite as *I Loved You, I Loved You* has been written
in the last two hundred and fifty years."

"Thank you," Tolaat Shani breathed. "Thank you,
Mr. Blau."

"Your collection of poems deserves a niche in
world literature, I say. Bravo!"

"Thank you. I shall try to polish the poems to perfection before you publish them."

"Publish what?"

"Publish . . . the book . . . Mr. Blau. *I Loved
You, I Loved You.*"

"Look here, I never said I was going to publish your poems."

"But . . . you said . . . wonderful . . ."

"Yes, they are very nice. But who buys poems nowadays?"

"I'm ready to renounce my writer's fee, Mr. Blau."

"That goes without saying. But it's not nearly enough."

"I'll make a small contribution toward costs."

"A fat lot of good that would do me. Perhaps you suffer from some fatal disease, T.S.?"

"Why?"

"If I could put the book in a mourning jacket— 'the poet's last work'—that would push sales."

"I'm awfully sorry, but I'm healthy. At least for the time being. Maybe when the rains set in . . ."

"I can't depend on miracles."

"So what can I do?"

"Now, I don't want to force your hand, but after the painter Zungspitz lost his eyesight, people paid fantastic prices for his canvases."

"Well, I wear glasses . . ."

"T.S. You apparently have not yet grasped the principle of this thing. No work of art sells nowadays without hullabaloo and scandal."

"Say, Mr. Blau, I have an idea! I'll walk up and down Allenby Road stark naked with *I Loved You, I Loved You* under my arm."

"A hoary old trick. The sculptress Gizella Glick-Galgal has already stripped twice on Dizengoff Circle with an eye on her forthcoming exhibition. They say she will sell all her statues. You've got to get up early to get somewhere, my boy. Can you play the trumpet?"

"Not yet."

"That's a pity. So the only thing we can do is get violent. After the first unfavorable review you'll kick in the teeth of the reviewer. OK?"

"Anything you say, Mr. Blau. But I'm afraid they'll only praise my poems."

"Oh, hell! Try to think. Perhaps you have some disease after all?"

"I'm desolate, but as I said . . ."

"Or perhaps there was some insanity in your family? That should be a great help. When Joseph Melamed went out of his mind and was locked up, they sold three editions of his novel."

"Lucky devil!"

"That wasn't just luck. He realized that to push sales you need publicity. Are there any love poems in the collection?"

"Don't you remember, Mr. Blau?"

"I have not read your poems yet. But if there are daring, realistic descriptions, something could be done."

"No, Mr. Blau! I'd rather jump from a rooftop."

"That's an idea! 'Disappointed in his love, poet commits suicide.' Not bad at all. You could dedicate a poem to Brigitte Bardot."

"Why not? Who is she?"

"Never mind. All you have to do is write on the flyleaf: 'To my eternal love, B.B.' "

"All right."

"You know, I begin to like your book, T.S.! We'll leak it to the press that you did two years for bigamy."

"That won't do. It happens to be true."

"Too bad. Is there anything anti-religious in your poems? Some offensive comment on Moses' character? The religious are very touchy on such matters . . ."

"I don't remember. But I could add it."

"Splendid. If we can get the Rabbinate to ban your book, two editions of it are as good as sold."

"Thanks, Mr. Blau, thanks."

"Don't thank me yet! That's not all. Tonight you'll get yourself arrested for gate-crashing, smash a few windows, blow a trumpet in the men's room of the Dan Hotel, undress and catch TB."

"I'll try."

"Curse the Government, get converted and leave the country."

"All right."

"Don't come back, T.S., before you are a complete lunatic."

"That should be easy, Mr. Blau."

❧ *This is a story written in a minor key about a little boy who did more for Israeli locksmiths than all the burglars combined.*

To Each His Fun

One evening not long ago we invited the Lustigs for a 7:30 P.M. tea. They brought Shragele, aged six and a half, along, though we had not invited him. As a rule, we are not too keen on parents dragging their offspring along, though it must be admitted that Shragele was very well behaved and only roamed through our apartment, examining everything. We talked with the Lustigs about nuclear warfare and the high interest rate. It was rather boring. Then suddenly we heard—really, I don't know how to say it and stay within the bounds of polite conversation—anyway, we heard Shragele . . . you know . . . flushing the water . . . in the toilet.

As a matter of fact, there is nothing special in this, a healthy kid should do such things, but the Lustigs became terribly alarmed and reeled as if they had received a blow.

"Shraga," the parents yelled, "what was that?"

"The key to Uncle's wardrobe," the kid replied calmly and smiled meekly. The Lustigs grabbed the boy by the ear and dragged him toward the key-bereft wardrobe, scolding him all the while.

"We hate to talk about this," Mr. Lustig finally unburdened his heart to me. "Shragele is quite a normal kid, except for a strange habit he has, a very odd habit indeed. If Shragele spots a key, he feels compelled to drop it in there. Only keys, nothing else! We are at a loss as to what to do. Acquaintances told us that we should simply ignore him, behave as if we didn't care, and in the end the kid would be cured by himself. We did so, but the only result was that we were left without a single key in our house."

"Tell me, Shragele," I called the little culprit, "why do you flush down keys?"

"Dunno," Shragele answered dreamily, "I simply like to do it."

"We even consulted a psychiatrist," Mrs. Lustig complained. "He questioned the child for two full hours and in the end asked us whether we had ever spanked him with a key when he was little. I told him that a key was much too small for that, whereupon we started arguing until we suddenly heard water being flushed down . . . We had to phone a locksmith . . . because Shragele had locked us in. The psychiatrist had a nervous breakdown."

Just then we again heard the ominous noise. We found that the key to our main entrance was missing.

"Do you live very high up?" the unfortunate parents asked.

"No," I answered, "only a yard or two above ground."

They departed through the window and promised to send a locksmith. I was left on my own, musing. After a while I suddenly took the key to my room and flushed it down the toilet. So help me, there is something in it!

🌺 *While this book was being written, our son Amir grew up miraculously and reached key-flushing age. He specialized—of all things—in kindergarten keys, a symbol of resistance to the country's babies.*

Show of Force

If you see two people in our suburb engaged in a heated debate in the middle of the street, you may bet your last penny that they will wind up discussing Topic No. 1: "Will Amir Kishon go to kindergarten, or won't he?"

The odds in favor of "He won't go" are currently three to one. Our little domestic problem has by now become public domain, since the neighbors, before going to town, have fallen into the habit of asking us through the window: "Is he staying home?" And Amir stays.

Of course, it has not always been like that. When we first took the brat to the neighborhood kindergarten —in early October, if I'm not mistaken—he immediately joined the other tots, ran around with them gaily, built castles of plastic blocks, danced to the tune of an accordion. In other words, he was still green and inexperienced in the ways of the trade. By next day he had found his sea legs.

"I'm not going to kindergarten!" Amir yelled and crinkled his nose. "Daddy, Mummy, not kindergarten! Not kindergarten! No! No!"

We asked why not kindergarten, you felt wonderful at kindergarten, didn't you? But the kid could provide no factual information. He simply did not want, refused to go. He would leave the country, but not go to kindergarten. Amir is an old hand at howling, and once he pulls out all the stops, he achieves woofs and tweets most uncommon for a sound system of his size.

The Seligs did not conceal their disapproval of our weakness.

"Fiddlesticks," Erna scoffed on the stairs. "The child will not agree to anything in this world except *faits accomplis*. Don't argue with him, take him to kindergarten and be done with it."

We respected this forceful woman for her courage. Here at last was someone who would not stand for any hanky-panky. A shame, really, that she has no children. Under her influence, we bundled Amir into the car and took him for a ride which ended at the gates of the kindergarten. Our offspring let go with full-throated blasts, but we just couldn't care less. We shook hands, the wife and I, well satisfied. So he's crying? Let him cry! That's what his throat is for, isn't it? Only after a while, a whole minute later, the question all the same arose in our hearts: Is he still crying? We returned to the kindergarten at a run to find the student hanging on the iron bars of the gate, shaking it with all his might, or, rather, shaking himself.

"Mummy, Mummy!"

Power politics thus failed dismally. Violence breeds violence. The news spread like wildfire: again he didn't go.

And then, as always in true-life stories, events took

a decisive turn.

On that evening we were invited to visit the Birnbaums, who live at the other end of the street, a nice couple, nothing special, mind you, but still . . . Conversing pleasantly, we told them about the Case of the Lost Kindergarten.

"He refuses to go," we concluded. "Not for a king's ransom!"

"Of course not," allowed Mrs. Birnbaum, a highly cultured woman. "You are simply trying to force your will on him, as if he were a trained seal. Look, our Gabi, too, refuses to go to kindergarten, but it would never occur to us to force him. We'll wait patiently until he himself asks us to take him. If we behaved differently, the child might take an aversion to school as well, develop a mental block to learning in general. We won't force him. True, this causes certain difficulties at home, you lose some time, but it's worthwhile if the result is a well-balanced child."

We were green with envy.

"And do you succeed with your system?"

"And how!" thus our hosts. "From time to time we ask Gabi offhand: 'Gabi, how about kindergarten tomorrow?' and that's all. If he says no, that's all right with us. One day, I'm sure, he himself will ask to be taken there. The cold war has to be fought out to the end."

Gabi stuck his head through the door. "Daddy, put me to bed."

"Come here, Gabi, shake hands with the gentleman," thus Birnbaum. "He, too, has a little boy, named Amir."

"Yes," thus Gabi. "Put me to bed."

"Soon."

"Now!"

"First be a good little boy and shake hands with the gentleman."

I shook Gabi's hand. A nice kid, tall and well built, with a striking resemblance to Rock Hudson, except that Gabi was a little older. A two-day stubble covered his face.

"You'll have to excuse us." Birnbaum and son started for the nursery.

"Gabi," Mrs. Birnbaum asked casually, "don't you want to go to kindergarten tomorrow?"

"No."

"As you like, my dear. Good night."

We were left with the mother.

"As a matter of fact, I don't mind his not going." Mrs. Birnbaum confided. "He's of military age and would not get along with those babies."

We left the Birnbaums in a pensive mood. With all due respect to our hosts' pedagogic methods, we could not quite approve of the result. That stupid kindergarten, we decided, was causing altogether too many complications; it had become the central problem of our lives. As a matter of fact, who says one has to go to kindergarten? Had I gone to kindergarten when I was a kid? Of course I had. So what? We'd have to rid ourselves of this nightmare.

The family doctor only confirmed our doubts when he declared: "Anyway, it's quite dangerous to send kids to kindergarten now. They infect each other with all sorts of summer diseases."

We summoned the student with hard-to-describe relief in our hearts. "Amir, you're in luck," we told him, "the doctor won't let you go to kindergarten because you could catch all kinds of terrible diseases. So that's the end of kindergarten, and good riddance!"

Since then we have no more problems with kindergarten. Amir goes there and sits all day long, waiting for the microbes. Wild horses could not drag him away. And whenever our admirers ask us how we turned the trick, we only raise our brows slightly and answer: "By medical methods."

🌷 *As expected, Amir's attitude toward TV has also changed since the first pages of the book when he still served as a pretext for the purchase of the despicable set. Nowadays the alert kid is ready to bump off anybody who stands between him and the silver screen. He'll probably liquidate us once he's tall enough to reach the knobs.*

The Longest Night

"Every miracle lasts a week," it says in the Book of Genesis, and rightly so. Take television: the first few weeks we were absolutely spellbound and didn't leave it for nights on end. Today? It's true we still sit in front of it for nights on end—but spellbound? Ridiculous, we've completely got over it. The trouble is that our house stands on top of a hill, which makes for rather good reception. If Cyprus, say, has one of its better days, it's quite intoxicating. The real victim of this technical success is Amir. It's rather morbid, really: sometimes this hypnotized child sits facing the screen for an hour, his eyes fixed in a dead stare on the words "*Israeli Television Broadcasts.*" If one remonstrates with him, he emits a grunt without taking his eyes off the screen: "Pchsssst!"

"Naturally, it isn't very healthy for a tot of five to be sprawling in front of the set day after day till midnight, because next morning he's going to get to kindergarten on all fours. Especially since Cyprus started their

instructional series *The Angel's Adventures* and our son
is being instructed night by night on how to commit
murder without really trying. His bedroom has to be
floodlit, he's scared of getting into bed, and even then
he can't fall asleep, but just lies there wide-eyed, waiting
for the killers, let them come already.

"That's enough," thus my little wife one evening.
"Eight o'clock, Amir's going to bed!"

It seems that, rather than a fact, this was but the
desire of a mother's heart.

Amir, that supreme master of delaying tactics, this
time surpassed himself with his high-frequency yells.
What's more, he activated his reverse throat-siren and
achieved an admittedly lethal effect.

"I won't go to bed!" our brat split our eardrums.
"Wanna see TV! Te-le-vi-sion!"

"You'll be dead beat," says his mother. "Go to
sleep, Amir, it's late as it is."

"And you? For you it isn't *too* late?"

"We're grownups."

"So go and work!"

He knows Russian too, a few choice expressions.

"You *can*," thus the harrowed child, "and I *can't?*
Why-hy?"

"Maybe you're right, son," I replied with the diplomatic instinct of a habitual father, "We'll go to bed
too."

And with that we switched the set off, made a big
show of yawning and went and pajamaed ourselves. The
trouble was that right then Cairo was giving *I Love
Lucy.* We therefore planted a smacking kiss on the
forehead of Amir, drowsy in his bed like a little angel,

and went—albeit on tiptoe—straight back to the living room. Softly we switched on the set, and in a few seconds the screen darkened with the familiar figure of our son Amir, standing before us, his face contorted with justified rage.

"Aha!" yelled our son. "I'm supposed to sleep and they can have a good time! *Liars!*"

"Daddy never lies!" his mother chided him. "We were checking the set for something and now we're all going to bed. Good night."

And then we all went to bed and fell asleep on the spot.

"Ephraim," whispered the woman, all asleep, "I think we can go back to the living room soon . . ."

"Shsh! He's coming."

Through half-lowered lids I saw my son's figure hugging the wall of the dark hallway on the way to the open door of our room. I began snoring and the little woman also made a good show of stertorous breathing. Reassured, Amir went back to bed to be afraid of murderers. We waited another few minutes in case of a double-check; then, as the area remained quiet, we crawled cautiously back to the set.

"Keep the sound off!" hissed the woman.

A bright suggestion. The picture's the thing, after all, and the words can be guessed at with a bit of effort at lip-reading. But in that case the picture's got to be sharp, right? The woman turned the light-dial as far as it would go. In fact, it grew dark at once, as she had turned on the sound, which burst from the set with the roar of the lion before Androcles removed the thorn from its paw.

It would be hard to describe in colloquial English the expression on Amir's face as he burst into the living room like a tornado.

"You sneaks!" He threw himself on the floor. "Sneaks, all of you! Why? Why-hy-hy?"

Just for punishment he sat with us all through *Peyton Place* and watched, sobbing, two belly dancers from Amman as well. Next day he dragged himself to kindergarten with his eyes shut and fell asleep in the middle of "Hava Nagilah." The teacher advised us to take him to the Sick Fund Clinic, since she thought he might have been bitten by the tse-tse fly or something.

"That's done it!" thus my wife. "We'll sell the set!"

"Okay, go ahead," the child yelled.

So nothing. We didn't sell the set or anything. However, on that long night we switched the set off at 8:15 sharp and went in a body to brush our teeth, each of us watching the others out of the corner of his eye, then dropped into bed like stones. It's true that I placed a tiny alarm clock, set to go off at 9:30, under my pillow, since we wanted to pass the double-check convincingly asleep. It went off quite well. The muffled whir of the clock woke us at the appointed hour and in the darkness we stole back toward the silver screen. Which is when the woman hit her head against something.

"Great heavens," she breathed. "He's locked us in!"

As I tried opening the door on the inside, I heard a creaking sound on the outside. Our son had put a chair in front of our door to serve as an alarm signal in case of treachery. He's gifted, our child, no doubt he's gifted.

He just isn't normal. And Cyprus was running Nelson Eddy and Jeanette MacDonald, *oi!*

"Wait," I rapped out, "I'll get in through the balcony!"

I tore through the window, jumped into the garden, clambered catlike over the living-room balcony, stuck my hand through the wire screen, opened the door, moved the alarm chair and set the woman free. All this didn't take more than twenty minutes. We switched on the set with feeling, but without the sound, naturally. Amir's region was quiet—too quiet, even. On the screen Nelson and Jeanette were singing an impressive visual duet with Greek subtitles. The tension was unbearable.

"Hey," I suddenly whispered to the little one, "something's going on."

"Ephraim!"

The woman leaped to the set and turned it off with a flick of her wrist. I dropped flat behind the couch. The silhouette of Amir, armed with a long stick, was outlined in the corridor on its way to the closed door of our bedroom. I looked at the woman flattened against the wall and signaled her not to move, but she was frozen anyway. Amir examined the chair, climbed up on it and sniffed around like a bloodhound. "We're selling," I said to myself, "we're selling the set tomorrow."

"Hello," Amir called sharply. "You asleep there?"

He repeated this question a few times, and when no reply came from within he opened the door.

I put the light on in the living room. Yes, that was the end.

"Ha-ha, Amirkele," I called jestingly toward my

son. "We fixed you, eh?"

Why go into details? I didn't mind the blows, they didn't hurt, but I guess the neighbors heard it all. Amir, in an atrocious mood, took his bedclothes and moved into the living room, pitching his tent in front of the television. In a way, we could see his point. His faith has been shaken, apparently. Also, ever since the incident he only calls us cheats, and he stays by the set till dawn. And what's wrong with that, actually? Kids breaking into villas and tormenting cats is better? If the boy wants to see television, let him see television, *gesunterheit*. We're selling the wretched thing anyway tomorrow, in a few days, sometime. We'll sell it. And buy a new one.

🌺 *The Hebrew switchboard operator as a rule is a twiggy Sabra girl with basilisk eyes and three arms. She wears brown sweaters, coughs in the morning and hates us. Toward noon the situation becomes unbearable and often flares into violence. Any attempt at mediation between us is bound to end in a fiasco. We are happy to barely maintain the cease-fire line during the loudly ringing summer months.*

The Hot Line

The confrontation of giants generally starts as soon as we dial and the Hebrew switchboard operator lifts the receiver on the other side of the barricade and says;
". . ."

That is, she doesn't say a thing, she only lifts. She generates silence, an eerie, ear-splitting silence. In the best of cases we hear far away in the background Grinspan's faint voice pleading with the trucking company to next time, for goodness' sake, send the bill to his new address, not like last Friday . . .

"Hello," we shout into the receiver, "hello!"

The Hebrew switchboard operator registers our voice above Grinspan's, but keeps us in cold storage for the time being. She quietly hopes that we are calling from a public phone out in the street and thus won't be able to leave the instrument. Because at home there is mobility: one can leave the silence to drown itself, go to the kitchen, prepare a sandwich, open a bottle of beer and return to the telephone equipped for a long siege.

"Hello," we say, munching rye bread, "hello!"

Sometimes at this juncture there is a response. After all, there is nothing personal in the Hebrew switchboard operator's elemental hatred, she simply hates the world-at-large which is trying by a thousand ruses and tricks to get at her switchboard. The confrontation becomes personal only after she identifies herself:

"729556, good morning!"

She never mentions name or address, this being a closely guarded secret known only to a chosen few. One may obtain the name, but not over the telephone. So, for the time being, there is only a number—and that's that.

"Hello," we say, "may we speak to Mr. Zerkovitz?"

"To whom?"

We check the slip of paper in our hand. There is no mistake, this is our number, all right.

"To Zer-ko-vitz."

"Yes, sir."

Here we hear the plop and crackle of myriads of plugs being inserted and extracted, then contact is established. And quiet. The world of silence returns in all its majesty. Maybe there is a little Zerkovitz, maybe there isn't. You never know. Only time will tell. We crouch down next to the instrument and hum marching songs. This is what the astronauts feel on the other side of the moon, utterly cut off from mankind.

"Hello," we say from time to time, "hello!"

We also knock a bony knuckle against the receiver and breathe some life into it. Fifteen minutes later we get the message, put down the receiver and break the umbilical to limbo. But since it is imperative that we speak to Zerkovitz (as a matter of fact, we only want his brother-in-law's phone number), we go back and spin the dial with renewed vigor. This time there is an immediate response:

"So let Naphtali take the parcel after four o'clock," the Hebrew switchboard operator says, "I'm not going to drag something to the bus station every day, excuse me, hello, 729556, good morning!"

We remove the cobwebs from our memory. Did we ever ask the switchboard lady to take any parcel anywhere? Surely that's Naphtali's job, isn't it? Let Naphtali take that thing at 4:00 or even 4:30, who cares?

We try not to be too aggressive. "Hello," we say. "I asked for Zerkovitz."

"Who?"

"Zer-ko-vitz."

"Who wants him?"

Now she has to know. In our previous call we managed to slip through her net, but this time there was something in our voice which awakened her inborn mistrust. The barrier is down, the identification parade on. We ponder carefully what to tell her: this is the Electric Corporation, Dr. Shay-Shenberg, he doesn't know me, we're childhood pals . . .

In the end we simply say: "Amnon."

Amnon always gets through. Amnon is lethal. The Hebrew switchboard operator relaxes, again there is a lot of promising crackling on the line, and in a matter of seconds we get the all-pervading silence. This time we don't waste precious minutes unraveling the meaning of the deadly lull, but open the book *Hannibal—*

One Man Against Rome and cross the snow-bound
Alps with the legendary warrior. Goodness, what a fantastic expedition it was, to take a whole caravan of frost-
bitten elephants across the mountains, along the rivers,
through storms and thunder . . .

At the very gates of the Imperial City we pull up in
the idle hope of being admitted to Zerkovitz's presence
instead.

"Hello," we shout into the receiver, "hello!"

Far, far away, perhaps across the great ocean, in the
heart of New York City, somebody twitters in Yiddish.
Somebody to whom the Hebrew switchboard operator
is giving a chance. Ours is a lost case, we are worse off
than Naphtali. Too much bitterness has accumulated in
these last few minutes. If we could only have met face
to face, outside office hours, Shula and we might have
found a common language, conceivably we'd have
courted her, never mind her skinniness, marriage is a
possibility, children, alimony. But as things are now,
with our lines stalemated, we have neither present nor
future: she's a switchboard operator and we're just one
of the dialers, cat and mouse. Not that we feel any ani-
mosity toward her, certainly not; as a matter of fact, we
respect Shula, are awed by her power, only there's no
communication between us. The best we can do toward
re-establishing relations is to put down the receiver and
swear, then dial her number again in this decisive
round.

"Miss," we say pointedly, "why do you let me wait
half an hour without answering?"

"Who's that?"

"Amnon. Three quarters of an hour ago I asked for

Zerkovitz . . ."

"He isn't in, sir!"

"Then why didn't you say so?"

"I'm telling you now!"

"When is he coming back?"

"Don't know."

"Where is he?"

"Don't know."

"Does he work there at all?"

"Don't know."

"May I leave a message?"

Here she takes leave of us with a deft flick of her wrist and it's all over. Luckily. Because our anger burns so fiercely in these critical moments that we clearly feel that if this conversation went on for another minute, we'd slip off our coat, jump into the telephone, crawl through the wires right into the switchboard and throw ourselves snarling and growling at Shula. It would be a fight to the end. Shula's manicured fingernails would scratch deep furrows into our cheeks, while our fangs would probe for her jugular vein, and thus we'd roll on the floor amid primeval grunts of Zerkovitz and murder. Yes, this is what's going to happen one of these days. It's only a matter of time. Political solutions are no longer possible.

❧ *Sport is becoming even more popular with the masses. Instead of twenty-two football players, two heavyweight wrestlers are quite sufficient nowadays for drawing twenty thousand sports-loving Jewish spectators. The only problem is finding those two wrestlers, so anyone handy is roped in according to all the rules of catch-as-catch-can.*

Clash of Titans

"So that's how it works, Weissberger: you don't enter the ring normally, but by vaulting over the ropes, like a young leopard."

"Why?"

"Because you are the 'Terror of Tangier,' Weissberger—how many times have I got to tell you? Naturally, the spectators will boo you, whereupon you will make an obscene gesture toward them and kick one of the ringside spectators. The miserable wretch gets his nose smashed in."

"Is that certain?"

"What do you mean, certain? That's what he's paid for. Also, behaving like the rowdy you are, you push the referee aside and he drops on the boards of the ring."

"Poor fellow."

"Don't be sorry for him, Weissberger, he's getting three percent of the gate. He'll warn you, but you'll only laugh and shake your fist at him. Then an excited spectator throws a Coke bottle at you."

"Oi!"

"Don't worry, Weissberger, he'll miss you. It's not the first time he's throwing for me. The cops will at once hustle him out of the arena."

"Can they be trusted?"

"Don't be silly, yesterday we rehearsed this twice with the police. Now let's talk about our brutal fight. Right from the beginning, you'll trample underfoot the most elementary rules of fairness."

"Why?"

"Listen, Weissberger, do you want to become a professional wrestler or stay a beggar all your life? You'll tear out my ears by their roots and I'll flounder like a wounded salamander. Then you'll curse in Arabic . . ."

"Couldn't it be in Yiddish?"

"God forbid. You keep forgetting, Weissberger, that you are the 'Terror of Tangier'! You manhandle me in the most horrible way. A woman will get up in the second row and start shouting: 'I can't watch this any longer! The referee was bribed by the Terror of Tangier!' "

"That's a lie!"

"Don't be silly, she is the referee's wife. You've got to organize things beforehand. The referee will try to separate us, but you'll catch his head between the ropes and tear off his pants. He'll die of shame. The doctor will diagnose a heart attack."

"Good Lord!"

"Weissberger, for goodness' sake, stop wailing. The doctor, too, is organized beforehand. While a new referee is ushered into the ring, the spectators jeer you from all sides. You make another obscene gesture and stick out your tongue."

"Is that necessary?"

"It's customary. Then police reinforcements will arrive on the double."

"They . . . too . . . are in on it?"

"Naturally. At this stage our fight becomes bestial, you stick your fingers in my eyeballs and pluck them out . . ."

"I don't feel well . . . Perhaps someone else could . . ."

"Weissberger, be a man. Do you know what unemployment there is outside?"

"I don't like violence. I am only fat."

"Without violence how could you ever dream of winning?"

"I am going to win?"

"I said 'dream,' my boy. The 'Terror of Tangier' should beat Samson ben Porat? Have you gone out of your mind, Weissberger? True, you'll sit on me for a while, twisting my foot and causing me grievous pain, but when the new referee reaches the count of nine, I'll suddenly give you a mighty kick . . ."

"No . . . no . . ."

"It's in the scenario, Weissberger. You'll soar about six yards and get entangled in the ropes and then I jump on you and boom! eogh! finish you off, while the cheers of the audience make the rafters ring. The refereee declares me the winner and then you lose control over yourself and throw a chair at the referee."

"A chair?"

"Yes, there'll be a chair in the corner especially for

that purpose, iron-studded."

"All right."

"Wait! The chair will have to hit an old man sitting in the middle of the grandstand, whereupon the enraged crowd will swarm into the ring and lynch you, shouting: 'You're a stinking bull, Terror!' "

"Mama!"

"Weissberger, you're at it again? Nothing is going to happen to you, I promise you. Don't you realize that the public, too, is organized beforehand? They know that they've got to lynch you when the old man gets hit with the chair. Is that clear?"

"Quite clear. Still, maybe someone will after all discover . . . that it's all fixed . . ."

"What do you mean, maybe? I can't wait passively until someone maybe discovers it. I've seen to it that the police should open proceedings against me for cheating the public."

"That too . . . is planned?"

"Naturally. We need press play, my boy. I can't trust in miracles. Any more questions?"

"Only one: if everybody knows that it's all a fraud, why do they come? Twenty thousand people . . ."

"What do you mean, why do they come? They love sport, Weissberger, they love sport."

❧ *What's the difference between the plumber and the Messiah? The Messiah might yet show up one of these days. The Hebrew plumber never comes, unless he is forced at gunpoint. The fate of our dripping faucets depends on who is quicker on the draw.*

The Plumber

Some afternoons ago the innards of our kitchen tap burst and the water poured out of it with elemental force. I immediately went to the only plumber of the neighborhood, a certain Stucks, intending to ask him to the sick tap's bedside. Only his wife was at home, but she said he would come to my place at about noon. I waited for a while, but he did not come, so I went there again. Only his wife was at home and she said that though her husband had been home in the meantime, he could not come yet, as he had to go somewhere else. He would come to my place before evening.

Stucks did not come in the evening, so I went to him, but there was nobody at home. The neighbors said maybe the Stuckses had gone to the cinema, they did not know for sure. I left a note in the keyhole saying would Mr. Stucks please come in the morning because the tap was leaking badly.

Stucks did not come in the morning, so I went to his place and nabbed him just as he was about to go out. He said he was on his way to me, but now that we had met, perhaps I would agree that he shouldn't come till noon, because he had to go to the Municipality. He said he would come around one; I asked him if we could not move it to half past one, as this would be more convenient for me, but he said he was sorry, it was out of the question, it would have to be either one or not at all.

I waited until 3:00 P.M., but he did not come, so I went to his place. Only his wife was at home, but she said she would intervene with her husband on my behalf. I asked Mrs. Stucks when she thought he could come, and she answered as soon as he came home— right now he was working at the factory because the foreman was sick.

I waited at home for about two hours, but Stucks did not show up, so I just went to his place. Stucks was just having his lunch and said he had not been able to come because he had been busy all the time, but now he would just take a few bites and be with me in no time at all.

I waited until the evening, but he did not come, so I went to his place, but there was nobody at home. I sat down on the doorstep and waited for them to come home, although they didn't come till midnight. I asked Stucks why had he not come to repair the tap, so he said he had been busy up to now, but I had nothing to worry about, he would come without fail at half past seven in the morning. I asked him if he could not come at seven, but he said no, that was out of the question. In the end we settled on 7:15.

I waited until ten, but he did not come, so I went to his place. Only his wife was at home and she promised to remind her husband to come as soon as he returned. When I left she ran after me and asked who I was and what I wanted. I told her that the tap was leaking badly, could Mr. Stucks come at once? If he had promised to come, the woman said, he would certainly come. He had not come by noon, so I went to his place. He was just having his lunch and said he would just swallow a few bites and come.

"You know what?" I said. "I'll wait for you." Whereupon Stucks calmly finished a very substantial meal, rose, yawning, and said he was sorry, but he always had to take a nap after lunch, then went to the adjoining room. I waited in my chair until seven in the evening, when Mrs. Stucks said, oh yes, her husband had left long ago through the kitchen. But she would tell him when he came home that I had waited for him.

What's the use of all this running hither and thither? I decided to sit it out then and there. Stucks came home at nine and said he was sorry, but because of the weather he had completely forgotten about me, what was it that I wanted? Look, I said, if you don't want to come, say so. I'll go to somebody else to have the tap repaired, there are other plumbers in the neighborhood. "But why shouldn't I come?" Stucks said. "That's what I do for a living." He even gave his word of honor that he would come at seven sharp in the morning, one night more would make no difference.

Instinct took me to his door at 5:00 A.M. He was just setting out for the city with long, vigorous steps: he was on reserve duty for that day. Wait, I said, and joined him.

In camp I did not let him out of my sight for a moment. We trained together on difficult terrain, dismantled a few mines, then on the way home he said, excuse me, I'll just change into overalls and come.

I waited for a while, but he did not come, so I went to his place, but only his wife was at home, and she promised to tell him that I had been looking for him. He did not come in the evening, so I bought a slightly used pistol and went on waiting for Stucks until noon. Stucks came home, then lay down for his customary nap. I asked him whether he would object if I handcuffed his left arm to my wrist. He said, go right ahead.

We slept for about half an hour, then set out for my place. On the way Stucks unexpectedly pulled his arm out of the handcuff and started running. I fired a burst at him. He returned the fire, but then ran out of ammunition, came out with raised hands, and repaired the tap.

This morning it started dripping again.

❦ *This little drama with the Shakespearean title strives to describe a very special situation indeed: the Hebrew plumber has come by mistake and in a moment of complete abandon has even repaired the dripping faucet. Now the time has come to pay him his well-earned wages. In this context the kind reader should remember the Chinese hangman's favorite torture, in which water drips at a measured beat on the victim's skull.*

As Much as You Like

CAST: *Kishon*
Mrs. Kishon
Stucks

STUCKS (*Walks up slowly and stops in front of Mr. Kishon, who is reading his paper. Clears his throat*): Well, Mr. Kishon, I fixed that bathroom tap. It wasn't an easy job, so help me, but that tap won't drip again, Mr. Kishon, I'm telling you, Mr. Kishon. I had to file down the cylinder a little bit, but I won't charge you for the filing, Mr. Kishon. I put in two new tipple rubbers, they'll hold the water as its never been held before . . .

KISHON (*Goes on reading his paper*)

STUCKS (*Drops his tool kit with an ear-splitting crash*): So, as I said, I finished the job, Mr. Kishon, I finished it completely. (*silence*) I absolutely finished. I finished the job, damn it. Are you deaf?

KISHON: What? Oh, thank you very much, old boy, all right, goodbye.

STUCKS: I said, I finished with that tap!

KISHON: Well, about time, too!

STUCKS: Why, "about time, too"?

KISHON: Look here, old boy. You had me come to your place for a whole month before you did me the honor of repairing this blasted tap.

STUCKS: That's because I'm so busy, Mr. Kishon. I'm always in a hurry. I'm always on the run. I haven't got a minute. What minute? Half a minute I haven't got. And why is that tap blasted?

KISHON: All right, so it isn't blasted.

STUCKS: Then why did you call it blasted?

KISHON: All right, I'll apologize to the tap. All right?

STUCKS: One has to watch one's language, Mr. Kishon. One never knows when and where!

KISHON: That will do, old boy, how much do I owe you?

STUCKS (*Takes out paper and pencil*): Well, let's see . . . I put in two new tipple rubbers . . . I won't charge you for the filing . . . (*Pulls out big watch from his pocket and looks at it*) It's now six thirty. Let's see. Because that tap is going to hold the water, Mr. Kishon, you don't have to worry. So maybe pay me, Mr. Kishon, let's say—as much as you like.

KISHON: Just tell me your price, old boy, we won't quarrel over it, right? (*Slaps his back*)

STUCKS: Right. (*Suddenly he slaps Kishon's back*) Because I fixed that tap, you know I fixed it beautifully. It's going to last, Mr. Kishon, as long as you live.

KISHON: Splendid.

STUCKS: It may even last five years!

KISHON: Fine. But now really tell me, old boy, how much do I owe you?

STUCKS: Right. Now I really got to tell you. It's getting late. So, Mr. Kishon, if you, too, think that I fixed it properly, pay me—as much as you like.

KISHON: You see, old boy, now this I don't like. What do you mean, "as much as you like"? I have no time for making calculations. You fixed the tap nicely and you'll just as nicely tell me that you charge for that so much and so much . . .

STUCKS: How much?

KISHON: So much and so much and so much. That's how civilized people do business, right?

STUCKS: Right. You are absolutely right. That's how civilized people do business.

KISHON: But this is ridiculous, so help me. Tell me, old boy, how much do you usually charge for fixing such a small tap?

STUCKS: It wasn't such a small tap.

KISHON: All right. For such a big tap.

STUCKS: It wasn't so big either. (*Shows size of tap on palm of his hand*) It was about this big. A medium-sized tap, two inches . . .

KISHON: So for a two-inch tap.

STUCKS: More than two inches.

KISHON: For a tap more than two inches big.

STUCKS: It could have been even three inches. I couldn't swear to it. Let me check. Just a second! (*Prepares to return to bathroom*)

KISHON (*Stops him*): For all I care, it could be a thousand inches big, old boy.

STUCKS: No, Mr. Kishon, it certainly wasn't a thousand inches big. There is no such thing. I'm almost sure that tap was between two and three inches big.

KISHON: All right, old boy, so how much do you get for fixing a tap between two and three inches big?

STUCKS: You mean the repair, Mr. Kishon?

KISHON: That's right.

STUCKS: It must have been three inches after all. Now I'm sure.

KISHON: For goodness' sake, how much do you get?

STUCKS: That differs from case to case, Mr. Kishon. Some people appreciate honest work. Others—quite to the contrary, Mr. Kishon—are stinking misers, dirty swine, miserable—

KISHON: How much does someone pay who isn't such a swine?

STUCKS: Such a person is not just a swine, Mr. Kishon, but also a stinking miser, a dirty swine, a miserable crook, that's what such a person is.

KISHON: How much does a person pay who is not a stingy swine, a dirty crook, a miserable, despicable, depraved miser, how much does he pay?

STUCKS: He always pays more.

KISHON: But in terms of money?

STUCKS: Of course in terms of money. I don't take checks.

KISHON: Listen, old boy, if you think you'll succeed in driving me out of my mind, you are very much mistaken! (*To his wife, who has just entered*) Come here for a minute, darling. I don't think I can take this much longer. (*Draws her aside, and from here on they talk in whispers*) I haven't the faintest idea how much to pay this idiot for fixing that tap.

MRS. KISHON: How much does he want?

KISHON: "As much as you like." He's trying to be smart. I know his kind. All the same, what do you think, how much should I pay him?

MRS. KISHON: How long did he work?

KISHON: I know? I didn't check it with a stop-watch. Maybe half an hour. But that idiot also put in some sort of . . . what-do-you-call-it, some . . . fix-it rubber . . .

STUCKS (*Whispers from the other side of the room*): Tipple rubbers, two of them.

KISHON (*Goes on whispering*): Yes. He put in two tipple rubbers. And now who the hell knows how much you are supposed to pay?

MRS. KISHON: I think I know. If having your stockings repaired costs eighty piastres, he can't ask more for fixing that tap than several times that.

KISHON: That's what I thought. The barber, for instance, takes half a pound, but that's entirely different, he uses soap, but on the other hand, there is no tipple rubber, though of course the barber may cut you with his razor if he isn't careful.

MRS. KISHON: I don't shave.

STUCKS (*Pulls out his watch, visibly impatient*)

MRS. KISHON: I don't think the tap can be more than two or three times more expensive than a shave.

KISHON: Wait! (*To Stucks*) Tell me, old boy, what's harder work for you, to shave or to fix a tap?

STUCKS: To fix a tap.

KISHON: Why?

STUCKS: Well, you see, shaving does not tire me, because with a good razor a weak beard like mine comes off easily. But such a four-inch tap needs a lot of handling.

MRS. KISHON (*Suddenly*): Stop! I think I've got it! (*Draws Kishon aside and from here on they again talk in whispers*) I know of a similar case. A few days ago they hauled a whole couch to the third floor for ten pounds.

STUCKS (*Whispers*): For twelve.

MRS. KISHON: All right, for twelve, what's the difference?

KISHON: Of course there is a difference. After all, we live on the second floor, and a tap is not nearly as heavy as a couch.

STUCKS: (*Again looks at his watch*) It's getting late. I'm in a hurry.

KISHON: So who's keeping you? Why can't you make up your mind, damn it, how much you're going to ask?

STUCKS: Sorry, I thought that was what you were whispering about.

KISHON: Do you think, old boy, that we have nothing else to worry about than your few pennies? We thought all along that you were going to tell us how much we owe you.

MRS. KISHON: It's always the person who gets the money who has to name his price.

STUCKS: So that's all right, Mr. Kishon, you are a writer, you get lots of money. So please tell me the price.

KISHON: You are stubborn, aren't you? This is too ridiculous for words, so help me! All right, two pounds? Four pounds? Four pounds twenty? A hundred pounds? A thousand pounds?

STUCKS: Now, now, now, what's the matter with you, Mr. Kishon? A thousand pounds for fixing a tap? That's a lot of money for poor people like us. True, I put in two new tipple rubbers, but I won't charge you for the filing, Mr. Kishon. I worked . . . (*Pulls out his watch*) All right, so pay me, Mr. Kishon—as much as you like.

KISHON: As much as I like? So listen carefully, old boy! You are not going to blackmail me. You may pull these tricks on people with weak nerves, but not on me! For me, to finish with people of your sort is as easy as this! (*Snaps his fingers*) So for the last time: how much do I owe you?

STUCKS (*Also snaps his fingers*): All right, let's see. I had two new tipple rubbers . . .

KISHON: You don't count the filing . . .

STUCKS: Yes, now I do. (*Pulls out his watch*) I fixed that tap, Mr. Kishon, very thoroughly . . .

KISHON: Why do you keep looking at that miserable watch?

STUCKS: Why is it miserable?

KISHON: N-n-not miserable!

STUCKS: Then why say so? One has to watch one's language, Mr. Kishon!

KISHON (*In a hoarse whisper*): Why do you keep looking at that watch?

STUCKS: True, why do I keep looking at it? There are no hands on it anyway. I also took out its works, needs a bit of filing, you know. A complete filing job . . .

KISHON: Is that so? (*Suddenly roaring*) How much do I owe you?

STUCKS: Look, Mr. Kishon, so that we shouldn't quarrel,

that there should be no haggling, no argument
. . . (*Shakes hands with Kishon*) Give me—as
much as you like!

KISHON: Tell me, old boy, do you really want to kill me?

MRS. KISHON: Please, don't excite my husband!

STUCKS: Who's exciting him? Pardon me, ma'am, am I
to blame if I'm so shy in business matters, not
brash like other people?

KISHON (*Shouting*): You are shy? You are a leech,
that's what you are! Listen, old boy, do you really
take me for a complete idiot?

STUCKS: No, no, I always exaggerate. Only yesterday I
said so to my wife. We were in the park with my
brother-in-law and little Hershele. (*The Kishons
collapse into chairs, exasperated*) Do you know
little Hershele? A wonder kid, a real darling, the
whole neighborhood is afraid of him. Well, to cut
a long story short, let's not waste time, I'm in a
hurry, I said to the wife, just as we came to the
first bench, I remember clearly, I said to the wife
. . . or maybe we had already passed the first
bench, I'm not quite sure, wait, let me think . . .
(*Walks up and down, trying to visualize their posi-
tions, mumbles to himself*) We were standing here,
so little Hershele came running this way . . .

KISHON (*As if coming out of a trance*): How much do
I owe you?

STUCKS: Let's say it was just in front of the first bench,
after all, the bench does not matter so much . . .

KISHON (*Jumps at him, grabs him by the throat and
shakes him*): How much do I owe you?

STUCKS: I can't do it for less.

KISHON (*Throttling him*): How much do I owe you?

STUCKS (*Choking*): As much as you can spare . . . for . . . this . . .

MRS. KISHON (*Separates them with great difficulty, screaming*): For God's sake, don't get so excited!

KISHON: You're right. This gangster is going to give me a heart attack. Here, old boy, take two pounds and beat it! (*Drops into armchair and takes up paper, but his hands shake*)

STUCKS (*Walks up to table with ponderous steps*): What? Two pounds? When the tipple rubbers alone cost three and a half? (*Bends over Kishon*) Some people are stinking misers, dirty swine, miserable crooks . . .

KISHON: Get out of here! (*Jumps up in a towering rage and throws Stucks' tool box, which had been standing on the table, to the ground. Ear-deafening crash. Tools scatter all over the room. Mrs. Kishon screams. Kishon drops, exhausted, into chair*)

STUCKS: Say, what's going on here? (*Lifts his soldering lamp*) Look, Mr. Kishon, now you broke my soldering lamp.

KISHON (*Utterly broken*): All right, I'll pay. I'll pay for the tipple rubbers, I'll pay for the filing, I'll pay for everything. How much do you get for the soldering lamp?

STUCKS (*Makes himself comfortable in the armchair, pulls out his watch*): As much as you like, Mr. Kishon . . .

CURTAIN

Ephraim Kishon

Ephraim Kishon is considered to be Israel's national humorist, and his books, films and plays have spread his fame throughout the world. Such books as Look Back, Mrs. Lot! *(1961),* Noah's Ark, Tourist Class *(1962) and* Unfair to Goliath *(1968) have been translated into almost every Western language, and* Unfair to Goliath *arrived Off-Broadway early in 1970 in the form of a review which was highly praised by the critics. In Israel his plays, produced under his own direction, have had record runs, and they have been performed on stage and television in other countries. The film* Sallah, *written and directed by Mr. Kishon, won many awards and was an Oscar nominee in 1964. He has been awarded the Israeli Nordau Prize, the Herzl Prize for Literature and the Sokolov Prize for oustanding journalistic achievement. Born and educated in Budapest, Mr. Kishon went to Israel in 1949 and now lives in Tel Aviv with his wife and three children.*